Inshore Fishing

Inshore Fishing

—its skills, risks, rewards

Stan Judd

Fishing News (Books) Ltd
110 Fleet Street
London EC4A 2JL

Set in 10/11 Plantin by Avontype (Bristol) Limited
and printed in Great Britain
by Redwood Press Limited, Trowbridge & London
71/7 10/11/P1

Contents

List of illustrations

Foreword

I am very glad to have the opportunity of saying a few words about this rather unusual book; because it is so seldom that one comes across a book about inshore fishing written by an inshore fisherman. It contains a very vivid and entertaining account of how and why the author took up inshore fishing as a way of life and how he managed to cope with the difficulties and frustrations with which a fisherman has to contend.

The story covers a period of some sixteen years which Mr. Judd has devoted to fishing and is centred on Mevagissey and the West Country generally.

Mr. Judd started from scratch, with no fishing tradition behind him but despite this he was able to overcome local prejudice and suspicion of newcomers and later was to become a leading hand in the fishing community and Chairman of the local fishermen's Society. All this speaks highly of the author's courage and determination and of his ability to learn all the technical skills involved in the various methods of West Country fishing.

This is well demonstrated in the later sections of the book where he describes how to fix and mend trawl nets and gives advice on handling drift nets and long lines; all these points are clearly illustrated by diagrams. The author has also included a description and plans for making a small cold store in which fish can be preserved; a piece of technical know-how which other fishermen living in the more remote districts may find very useful.

There are many good stories in the book and I particularly enjoyed Mr. Judd's sense of humour. I got a good laugh over the immaculate foreman in a canning factory who got sprayed with a mixture of pilchards and tomato sauce, to the delight of the staff! Then, too, there is the description of his first trip with old Lewis and that terrible old Britt engine, which despite its awkward lay-out and difficulty of handling was later responsible for saving the author's life. Another chapter, which anyone who has had to deal with boats will enjoy, is the saga of the "We'll Try"—a near disaster—which eventually became a success, due to sheer ingenuity, determination and guts.

Whilst inshore fishing predominates the book, the author wittily describes several other ploys he had to turn to, including driving a lorry at a china clay works, running pleasure trips for visitors, shark fishing and the difficult job of a travelling fishmonger. All these ex-periences have been grist to Stan Judd's mill, and his ability to make good friends is manifest throughout the book.

I was particularly interested in what he has to say about the Fisheries Organization Society of which I have had the honour to be Chairman since 1961 and I am, therefore, very glad Mr. Judd thinks we are doing a good job. The Society has been in existence for over 55 years and from a small beginning it is now the only officially accepted organization representing the interests of some 12,000 inshore fishermen in England and Wales of which 5,000 are in direct membership of our 100 affiliated Societies.

Mr. Judd's account of the setting up of Mevagissey Fisheries Ltd. is a typical example of the sort of service the FOS can provide. However, the success of the local society was largely due to Mr. Judd's deter-mination and drive. The figures he quotes in chapter 17 demonstrate how successfully it has progressed and are convincing evidence of achievement. It is true to say that, but for the existence of the society, Mevagissey would probably have ceased to function as a fishing port. This applies with equal force to many other small fishing communities where successful fishermen's societies have been established.

The FOS exists to help inshore fishermen, by encouraging them to co-operate in setting up their own local society either to market their own fish or provide some other services, such as transport to get their fish to market, or even to establish their own ice making plants. Apart from all this we maintain contact with all our societies so that both local and national fishery problems can be understood and representations on behalf of the fishermen made to authorities concerned.

I have spent most of my working life mixed up with fisheries and fishermen and I am firmly convinced that the interests of the inshore fishermen are best served by co-operating together if their indepen-dence is to be preserved. The inshore industry has undergone great changes in the past 50 years; vessels have become more sophisticated with better sea-keeping qualities, and many are now equipped with radar and echo sounders. Through all these changes over the years certain basic things have remained constant, namely the courage and craftsmanship of the men themselves, their independence and hardihood all of which are so clearly demonstrated in this book.

T. S. Leach, Chairman,
Fisheries Organization Society.

37 Denison House,
296 Vauxhall Bridge Road,
London, S.W.1.

Preface

I wrote this book for the same reason that I chose to go fishing, because I wanted to. I have no regrets for doing either, and I hope the reader will enjoy this simple yarn about a job which is really a way of life.

For those who seriously contemplate taking up fishing for a living, there may be a few helpful suggestions to be found here and there. For those who think inshore fishing is just a matter of popping in and out of harbour to scoop up fish when they feel like it, well, after reading this they may have a better understanding of the job and all the factors involved.

Although marketing, prices, boats, engines, fish finding equipment, ship to shore wirelesses and many types of fishing gear have vastly improved since I started fishing, the problem of actually catching fish is still a very personal thing, depending very largely on the fisherman himself, his knowledge, his aptitude, and above all his determination to succeed.

I shall never be a "Top Notcher" as they say in these parts, but as long as I catch my share and have an extra bit of luck now and then to smooth over the bad patches, to me it's all well worth while. For those people who visit Mevagissey, or any fishing village or port in the British Isles, I hope that after reading this book they may have a little better understanding of the people, the environment, also the problems and pleasures of inshore fishing.

Stan Judd

Mevagissey
Cornwall 1971

Chapter 1

I decide to go fishing

I CAME out of the army after two years' conscription in September 1950, at the ripe old age of twenty! I had been attached to the 18th Training Brigade, Royal Artillery, as an instructor on 25-pounder field-guns. It sounds better than saying I spent two miserable years in the "cake" being either chased around or chasing other poor blighters less fortunate than myself. I have heard it said that the army makes a man of you. What it did for me I shall never know, except I came out with three stripes, a pimply face and a hearty dislike of any form of regimentation.

An only child, I had the choice of going abroad into the Rhodesian Police (this had been laid on for me by the army) or staying at home and settling down. My mother and father were getting on in years as I had been a "late arrival" so as Father's health was very poor at that time, I was persuaded to stay at home with them and try my hand at being self-employed.

Before going into the army I had trained as an operating theatre technician, supplementing my rather poor pay by doing a lot of free-lance commercial art work, but two years later neither form of employment appealed to me very much.

We lived in the country, so with my father generously backing me financially I doddered along for the next three years keeping pigs and poultry, buying and selling stands of timber and underwood, then later manufacturing breeze or concrete building blocks. To my credit, I worked very hard, the country's economy was such at the time it was even possible to employ people and show a moderate profit. But alas, I was not happy; I spent most of my evenings consuming large quantities of beer and chasers in our local and wishing I had gone to Rhodesia.

We lived at that time on the outskirts of the small village of Crawley Down in East Sussex—a pleasant place but it was being rapidly developed, as was the town of Crawley a few miles to the west of us. By this time my father had retired, often expressing a wish to move to Cornwall, while Mother thought a smaller place to manage would be just the thing for her too. I had nothing to lose by falling in with their plans so we sold up and moved to Mevagissey in South Cornwall.

Just like that! It took four months from deciding to move until we had actually settled in at the other end.

Mevagissey was a compromise really. As a family we had always gone to the Isles of Scilly for our spring and autumn holidays, but we felt it would be a bit cut off if we moved there permanently; added to that, houses were hard to come by and the chances of employment for me limited with the exception of seasonal work.

Once we had moved into our new abode—a nice little semi-detached cottage in Cliff Street—I set to work doing a few necessary repairs, then redecorating inside and out. When this was finished I turned my attentions to the garden, a postage sized plot of land reached by scaling twenty-two almost vertical slate steps. I actually expended more energy going up and down to it than I did digging it! My evenings were usually spent catching pollack and bream from the end of the Island Quay (the Eastern protective arm of Mevagissey's outer harbour).

It was during one of these highly productive sessions that I made the acquaintance of "Tiny" Dick Pascoe. A young giant well over six feet tall, at that time a mere—no, I won't say what he weighed then as I often see him now and he's considerably heavier. He might playfully exterminate me. Great sense of humour has Dick! He originally came from Mullion Cove, much further to the West'ard, but then lodged at Mevagissey.

I mentioned to him that it was time I got a job, so he gave me an introduction to the foreman of the firm he worked for. I spent the following months driving a lorry on one of the china clay mining locations, taking loads of earth and rocks from one place, then tipping them at another.

It was the hottest summer for years, so after carrying a couple of loads in the morning we all looked like film extras in a war epic. Our faces would be caked with fine brown or grey dust, streaked with sweat rivulets; our clothing, whatever colour when we started out, was soon as picturesque as our faces, brown or grey!

Being a new boy I had been issued with an old Ford V8 tipper which had obviously been scrapped several months before, then recommissioned again. We were paid a basic wage per week plus a bonus on the number of loads carried, the tally being kept by a tipman. He also supervised the tipping operations and was responsible for placing and replacing the wooden baulks of timber which were used to stop the lorries from going over the edge. These, incidentally, were seldom used, as with nearly twenty lorries going at it, he couldn't keep up with us, and no-one would stop to help him move them! I heard on good authority later that year that an extra man was put on that particular tip to assist in maintaining timber stops and directing lorries at the edge—a sensible decision and not before time.

Many of the chaps in our gang had either new diesel or petrol tippers which were superior in speed and safety to my old banger, which had a job to struggle up hill empty. So it was very frustrating to be passed by other vehicles all day long—which left me five or six loads down every day. After a few weeks, I got friendly with the excavator driver, who remarked how well I was managing with my lorry considering its condition. I replied I could manage a lot better if he didn't put so much on, and from then on I had a much easier time—often trundling off only half full, and seldom with any quantity of heavy rock, which he kindly saved for the more robust vehicles.

Helpful Aid!

There was one chap in the gang nobody got on with. He didn't even like himself! My lorry's engine back-fired and caught fire one day. Another driver and myself were busy shovelling sand over it when the horrible character coasted by grinning from ear to ear at my misfortune. He had a brand new eight yard diesel tipper complete with two fire extinguishers in clamps at the back of his cab, and there they stayed.

I made a mental note of his conspicuous gallantry and then drove off in my car to the nearest phone to report the old dear had at last succumbed to the rigours of cross country carting. Later that day I wished I had let it burn, as a mobile workshop arrived, revived my smouldering wreck, made a few repairs, then pronounced it fit for further service.

My friend the excavator driver took the next step in ridding me of the monster. A few days later he picked up an enormous boulder, balanced it squarely on the edges of his bucket and then dropped it from a fair height into my lorry's battered body. The result was more than I had hoped for. With a sharp crack followed by a violent screeching sound, one side of my lorry sank gracefully to the ground, the side giving way as it laid over, spilling its load back from whence it came.

The excavator driver climbed slowly down from his cab looking as pleased as I was. "Don't ee worry old dear, chassis must have been cracked", he said. Then lighting the cigarette I had gratefully offered him, he returned to his machine looking more than satisfied at having rendered me such a service!

The following morning I was issued with another petrol engined tipper—this time an eight yarder, and about the fastest thing on four wheels in the whole area. With a full load I was able to overhaul most of the other lorries going up to the tip. We never overtook going down empty though, with the exception of the chap who had already incurred my displeasure. He, being the pig he was, would nip in front of several of the older drivers to get an extra load or two in during the

day, sometimes forcing them to stop rather than risk damaging their
vehicles on the very rough track's edge.

My chance came about a couple of weeks after I had the new lorry.
Matey had deliberately pulled out to stop me overtaking him up the
wide approach hill to the tip, so I dropped behind him again. When I
reached the top I was able to tip, then get away again before him, but
half way back to the excavation site I saw he was going to try to over-
take me. He chose a bad spot, for, as he pulled up nearly level with
me my foot happened to weigh heavy on my accelerator pedal, I then
being much fatigued by this time of the day! My lorry shot ahead and
sad to say "Snidy" as he had been nicknamed, had to leave the track;
his machine tore down a short steep slope to end up with a smashed
sump, front axle and radiator. He reported me to the foreman back
at the depot, who made enquiries but wisely took the matter no further.
It did get rid of "Snidy" though, for he was transferred to another site,
being replaced by a much older and more gentlemanly character.

So for three months I shifted Cornwall about by day and angled in
the cool of the evenings while watching the pilchard drifters leave the
harbour sometimes to shoot their nets within our sight in the bay or
to disappear over the horizon to re-appear after dark as a row of tiny
twinkling lights.

I choose Fishing for a Living

By this time I had definitely decided to go fishing for a living,
but it was easier said than done. I made many enquiries around the
harbour to see if I could get a berth on one of the boats, but these
resulted in me being openly laughed at or being given a look which did
not encourage further conversation on the subject! The more I was
rebuffed the keener I became, so by the middle of August I took the
plunge and bought a twenty-seven foot dandy boat called the *Joyance*.

Our neighbours at Cliff Street were an oldish fisherman and his
wife, Lewis and Florence Behennah. He had had a disagreement
aboard the boat he had been working on, so had come ashore until a
berth was available on some other boat when the winter's pilchard
season started. To my surprise he volunteered to come with me, and
so a short-lived but rewarding partnership was contracted.

I bought nets of all sizes, and sad to say, of all conditions. Once
the news got around that I was in the market for nets, I was offered
them it seemed from nearly everyone in Mevagissey. Some mesh
sizes were too large, some too small, some nets were too hard, some too
soft. It was always the large nets that were too soft and vice versa,
whilst others were so "ripe" with old age that a good spot of pilchards
would have carried them off the headropes never to be seen again,
every fish with a small cotton collar!

I spent a week boiling, barking, greenoiling and drying pilchard nets, followed by another week "taching" them together, then putting the cobles on. The best fourteen nets were stacked on the quay in a fleet by the Friday lunch time to be hauled aboard the next morning. Superstition was rife in those days and hauling aboard a fleet of nets on a Friday was likely to evoke all sorts of catastrophy, so Lewis's wishes were respected and Saturday morning was the proper time to do it.

I do not intend to dwell on the subject of superstitions except to say that when I first started fishing I was unimpressed by the stories I had heard. Sixteen years later I have learned much, but many events and the questions they pose remain unanswered. Coincidence or design? Who can say? Many events connected with the sea must remain mysteries for ever.

Learning the Hard Way

That particular Saturday morning, however, went off without serious mishap. A large group of fishermen watched Lewis and me haul our nets off the quay, then through the water to soak them thoroughly before stowing them carefully into the net room. Lewis put on a fine act. With head down and arms going like piston rods, seemingly miles of net came aboard. Every coble I stowed went in the wrong place! Every bunch of headrope went down tangled, but who was I to argue? I hung my head, tried vainly to keep up with Lewis whilst pretending to be oblivious of the audience who were enjoying every minute of what must have been an enjoyable free morning's entertainment. In fairness to the spectators, they willingly helped clear the nets from the pile and then threw down the cobles and straps as we came to them. During these operations there was a great deal of good natured banter, laced with sarcasm, Lewis being told not to go on so, and me to pull my finger out!

Chapter 2

My first catch
of pilchards

THE fine unbroken spell of weather continued. Monday was boiling
hot with a slow, oily, south easterly swell rolling straight in towards Mevagissey. Not a breath of wind disturbed the surface, although
far out in the channel there was obviously some wind which was
creating the motion that crashed in with monotonous regularity
against the great granite cliffs on either side of the harbour entrance.
I had a swim in the outer harbour at lunch time, then ate and retired
for a nap, I suppose I was too keyed up to sleep, so I lay on my bed
sweating in the afternoon heat wondering what my first night as a
fisherman would produce in the way of fish and surprises.

Seven in the evening was muster time. On the dot, I sauntered
round to the East Quay where the *Joyance* was moored. Fifteen
minutes later I wondered if Lewis had changed his mind as there was
no sign of him. How little I knew about fishing and the men connected
with it I was about to find out!

Picking up my copious bag of food I walked anxiously inward again.
Passing directly underneath the cliff wall I was aware of a row of
faces peering over the top intently watching my progress around the
harbour. A few more bunches of fishermen were clustered at the inner
corner. I furtively glanced at them to see if Lewis was amongst them,
they all stopped talking and stood staring at me as I went past. At last
I spotted Lewis, biscuit tin tucked under his arm, standing with a
large crowd of men in the middle of the jetty. He nodded to show me
he had seen me, then turned away again to continue his conversation.

No-one spoke to me, the rest of the men all stood around just
looking at me. Not nicely you understand, but scornfully, indignantly,
sadly or blankly. To make matters worse for me, I stood there feeling
very self-conscious in a brand new jersey, smock, sea boots, bright
red woollen bobble hat and a large shopping bag in my hand. In those
days it was an unheard of thing to go to sea with a shopping bag and
sporting a brightly coloured woollen hat on one's head. A properly
lashed biscuit tin and a flat cloth cap were the essential requirements,

sea boots optional but usually kept aboard the boat. I felt like a poppy in a cornfield, and in fairness to the onlookers, I must have looked like one!

After what seemed an hour but was probably only another five minutes, several groups of men left the main bunch, clambering aboard punts to scull out to various luggers laying at their moorings in the inner harbour. This was the signal for a general scramble. Lewis, pipe firmly clenched in the corner of his mouth, his cap pulled well down over his eyes, nudged me with his elbow muttering, "It'll be dark afore we shet in a minute" and ambled off round the harbour at a great rate of knots with me in hot pursuit a few paces behind.

Once aboard he had the legs unshipped, fenders in and the punt made fast to the stern before I had even found the petrol squirt which was needed to start the small motor. In my haste to appear at least an efficient engineer, I had already knocked the only engine room light bulb out of its holder with my head, at the same time slipping, grazing both my left shin and forearm on the port engine. The petrol squirt had shot from my hand to land somewhere at the back of the beyond. Happy days indeed!

Lewis's head appeared over the engine room, at the same time, blocking out the only source of light.

"If ee don get un gouren zun we'll av tue mur up again" he growled.

Starting that Motor

The motor was a single cylinder eight horse power Britt, twenty two years young. A black, forbidding lump of machinery with a very large rusty vapouriser at one end, and a large fly wheel at the other. It started on petrol, then, when warm, was changed over to run on paraffin. Starting was complicated. First, the carburretor had to be drained of any surplus paraffin before turning the petrol on. Then when this was done, the float chamber had to be tapped steadily as the petrol flowed in; if the float still did not seat properly a piece of fine wire was hung from the inlet pipe which was then pushed through a small hole in the top and jiggled about until the petrol stopped overflowing. After removing the sparking plug and thoroughly cleaning it with a wire brush, a generous squirt of petrol was shot into the plug hole before replacing the plug. The air valve cover was then unscrewed, several squirts of petrol shot into that before replacing the top. On the port side of the engine, in the most inaccessible place possible, was the decompression lever, which to function had to be pushed in, then held there with a small steel pin to retain it. The pin, I remember, had the same piece of thick tarred cotton twine tied to it the whole time I had the boat, and I suspect it was the original piece put on to save the pin from being lost when the engine was new! The needle was then unscrewed in the carburettor to ensure a good flow of petrol, the throttle opened, and most important of all, the ignition on the magneto retarded. If this was not done, starting was not only impossible, but highly dangerous to the person attempting it, as the engine would always backfire with tremendous force.

Well, having prepared the beast, all that was needed was manpower. With legs, back, arms and neck bent at various acute angles, an almighty effort would succeed in getting a loud bang, followed by a rapid puffing, rattling and clanking from all over the engine. If you were quick enough, the pin had to be pulled out of the decompression lever which was also pulled back, then held in the new position again by being re-pinned. Care had to be taken over this operation as the top of a finger could easily be crushed, as once the engine was going you could not lay over it to see what to do. If the last operation had been accomplished fast enough, petrol would again be squirted into the air intake valve until the engine ran steadily. If the gods were not smiling on you, the whole operation had to be repeated in sequence until it did go, but twice was usually sufficient unless it was a really bad day!

I never cursed that motor because I felt it could easily get its own back on me. It did, in fact, once definitely save my life, and got me out of serious trouble on a second occasion, both times when the larger main engine broke down completely in very bad weather a long way from home.

I had sized up the two engines during the fortnight prior to our first trip, so I was able to get the old Britt chuffing away first go, much to Lewis's surprise, I fancied.

Having anchored our punt in the outer harbour on the way out, I put the main engine into gear to facilitate easier starting, turned on the petrol, then one swing later we were off under full power, all twenty-three horse power of it! I still had the oiling wicks and drip feed box to attend to plus a generous squirt of oil all round on all the slides and open bearings, then changing both engines on to paraffin and adjusting the jets and ignitions I came up for much needed air. There was a continuous blue fug of smoke and fumes which poured out of the engine room hatch, but I swear no air ever went in to replace it!

I staggered around on deck trying to get my balance as the *Joyance* jumped, twisted and rolled over the swell. If this was fine weather, what was the rough stuff going to be like? Lewis stood in the stern sheets, tiller tucked between his legs watching me. I thought I detected a slight grin, or was it his pipe that made the corners of his mouth curl? I plucked up the courage to ask him how far we were going. He replied about an hour south and by east of Mevagissey, impressing on me carefully that the boat was timed off from abreast of Chapel

Point, a headland a mile south of Mevagissey. This was to ensure that if we set over a good distance to the West'ard with the ebb tide after drifting with the nets out, we would come to land on time, then ease down to ensure we did not run ashore if the weather came in thick or dirty during the night. My education had begun.

The rest of the fleet was strung out ahead of us. We had been the last boat out of harbour, but I suspected Lewis had purposely hung back to see first what was going on, which later proved correct. Only a few of the largest luggers had Kelvin Hughes fish finders installed in them at that time. We either had to rely on chasing them or on Lewis's experience. This was to stand us in good stead that evening, as it did during the weeks that followed. After an hour we drew level with some of the other boats, while on the back and to either side of us the larger ones were still searching, picking out the thickest of the fish shoals on their meters. Some of the smaller boats had already started to shoot, but Lewis obviously going to bide his time, started motoring away to the west side of the main bunch of boats.

The Lessons Proceed

We had only been running on our new course for a few minutes when Lewis said he had seen several pilchards "stoiting" around us.

I didn't know what that was, but having found out it was fish jumping clear of the water, soon started to spot them myself. Lewis also showed me a shoal of pilchards "riddling", that is swimming and just breaking the water with a sound like rain falling. I spotted a large shoal riddling ahead of the boat and pointed at them to show Lewis where they were located.

I was curtly told never to point, as other people were watching us and we weren't there to find fish for them to catch! Thus ended the second lesson.

We expected a breeze off from the land after sunset, so we turned and motored inwards for several minutes before slowing prior to shooting our fleet. I stopped the main engine off when told, retarding the ignition on the Britt to facilitate slow running; then, taking my position fore side of the net room, Lewis gave the order "Shet Away".

My job was to shoot the leach, the main bulk of the net, whilst Lewis shot the headropes, cobles, steered the boat and knocked the engine in and out of gear with a lever situated aft side of the engine room casing.

I was taken aback at the speed and agility of my shipmate. My left arm was ready to drop off before half the fleet had gone overboard but somehow I kept going until eventually the spring rope was shot, the end made fast and I went aft to turn off the engine. We didn't bother to hoist the sail and slew again as there was no breeze at all.

The boat lay slurping, sloshing, rolling and dipping with the spring rope hanging limply over the stern attached to a cleat.

That was when my real troubles started. Our little cuddy for'ard had a tiny hatchway which served as both entrance and ventilator. Being the junior I was delegated to light the primus stove and boil the kettle ready for our tea. By the time I had done this I felt decidedly ill. Staggering up onto deck I took deep breaths and after a few minutes began to feel a little better. Lewis called up that my tea was getting cold, so not wishing to appear too much of a tweeney I took a big gulp of fresh air and returned to the 'hole of gloom and doom'.

Lewis sat back as if in an easy chair in his own front room. He had taken his cap off, I remember noticing how white his balding head was in contrast to his deeply tanned face and neck. He held a large piece of saffron cake in one huge knarled fist, in the other was a mug half full of tea. Lewis sucked a mouthful of tea from his mug, then followed it up with a mouthful of the hard yellow cake which, whenever I had eaten stuff like it, had given me violent indigestion. A thin trickle of tea crept from one corner of his bulging mouth, then he sucked it back, dexterously poking in another load of yellow peril.

That did it! Deciding to die in the fresh air I summoned up enough strength to scramble out onto the deck once more to be violently sick over the side, having just made it in time. That over, I sat cold and miserable on the engine room hatch wondering why I could not die quickly, not expire slowly as I was obviously doing. After a while, Lewis came up with a cup of tea for me, so rather than offend him I gulped it down.

If it had been rubber it could not have rebounded from my stomach faster, I swear it came up with such force it ran out of my ears!

Lewis muttered something about wasting sugar and milk, then sat down to light his pipe and watch me popping over the side for a puke at regular intervals for the next hour. When it was dark and Lewis thought I was empty, he quietly told me to start up the engine. Weak and dizzy I managed it after a struggle, popping up for a repeat performance over the side as soon as it was going.

My job was to haul the boat astern by the headropes, hauling in the cobles and straps as they came along, stowing them as neatly as possible on the after side of the net room, while Lewis hauled the leach of the net over a long wooden net roller on one end of which was a pawl and ratchet which stopped the net rolling back over the side once it had been pulled in.

Rewarding Sight

My first sight of pilchards in the nets was a wonderful experience for me. The night was pitch black, while phosphorescence in the water

made every mesh appear as if alight with a brilliant whittish-blue flame,
After the first coble had been reached there was a solid mass of pilchards
in the net from the top to the bottom. It seemed to my inexperienced
eyes that there was one in every mesh, although I was not to see that
until later that winter. What a sight that was! As the net came alongside
the fish in it shone like a solid wall of light blue flame.

Lewis started tut-tutting, which was his way whenever annoyed or
worried.

"We're going to 'ave zum jam tonight" he informed me. I replied
that I thought we would have a good catch and that I didn't mind how
thick the pilchards came.

Starting to work and seeing the pilchards in our nets had made me
feel a lot better, so although I had a vacuum where my once well-filled
stomach had been, I must have appeared decidedly cocky to Lewis.

"Chah" he exploded, dropping the net, standing hands on hips
glaring at me quite savagely. "With these splats we'll 'ave round turns
end over end. Jam I tell'ee, nothing but bloody jam—Chah!"

With that off his chest he resumed his task with increased vigour.
He was right of course. After the first spot of fish the net went almost
blank for the length of a couple of straps with the exception of a few
scattered fish right at the bottom.

When spots of pilchards rise on a summer's evening they do one
of two things: either they spread out over a large area to bunch up
again and sink at daybreak or they tear around near or on the surface
in comparatively small, fast swimming shoals, often carrying the net
up and right over the headropes to mesh themselves in several layers
of the same net.

All our fish on the first night had been fast swimmers and highly
acrobatic. The net started coming up in rolls, white and silver with
pilchards so tightly skivered in that pieces of them flew all over the
place as we tore them apart in our effort to unroll the net. "Shake
away, don'ee look at 'em, get the bloody net square, don'ee thrash *too*
'ard—oh my Goor!"

I put up with his flow of orders, comments and scornful abuse until
we were all in around two the next morning with our centre fish berth
full to the top.

Lewis had worked like a man possessed, whilst I had at least kept
my temper and done the best I could. Looking back on that first night
I must have seemed a right Charlie to Lewis, to say the least!

"You'll get used to it"

We anchored in the outer harbour just after four the following
morning, as the tide was nearly low, and went ashore by punt. To my
relief Lewis told me that there was no need to come down too early

that morning as the buyer we were landing to would case our pilchards, then take them into their store by large punt. He added I was to be down quay by nine sharp, teatime would have done me. When I got home I just had enough strength left to wash, then crawl into bed where I immediately sank into a deep black oblivion.

It seemed only a few minutes later when I awoke to find my father shaking me hard telling me it was a quarter to nine. Falling out of bed then dressing, I staggered downstairs to find a very smug looking Lewis sitting talking to my mother. I later gathered he had told her I might make something, given long enough at it. I never knew whether he was being polite or sarcastic, perhaps just as well!

My first job that morning was to collect the fish tally from the buyer, just over eighty stone if I remember correctly, then I replenished the fuel and oil, washed the boat down and pumped out, while Lewis mended some holes made by sharks as they had passed, then repassed through our nets whilst having an easy feed the previous night. He had thrown the net with the holes in it out into the port waterway as we had hauled them in.

By lunchtime I was half asleep again, my face and eyes smarting and burnt by the creosote used in softening the harder nets, so after my lunch I had a good sleep until six that evening. At seven I casually strolled down to the harbour making my way straight to the jetty where I again saw Lewis standing with his bunch of mates.

My woollen hat was stuffed out of sight in my back trousers pocket. I wore shoes, and most important of all, I had a hastily acquired biscuit tin, neatly lashed, tucked under one arm. I still got my quota of queer looks, but one or two men nodded as I sidled up to Lewis. One of the men looked across to me and much to my surprise spoke. "Lewis says you'm a sticker boy—you'll get used to it in time".

I nodded back, trying hard not to appear too pleased at the remark. Lewis turned to me with a wicked grin on his weather-lined face "Come on Stan, the first five years are the worst".

I went off down the quay feeling ten feet tall and four feet wide, both statements were to turn out perfectly true—I did get used to it in time, and it took me just five years to conquer sea sickness—they were definitely the worst!

Chapter 3

Dahn lines, buffs and creepers

THAT season went well for all of us. The weather remained excep-
tionally fine until September and we only had an odd night in for
bad weather now and then.

The pilchards had moved right into the bays so we were able to
fish only a few minutes from the harbour at times, with a minimum
amount of net damage as the sharks seldom came right in to shallow
water, even though the bays were packed with pilchards. Occasionally
though, the outside boats of the fleet would get a pasting, especially
if fishing was heavy and they were a long time getting their nets in.

September came in still keeping very fine, but the pilchards had by
then started to move off to sea again and disperse. Catches dwindled
to a few baskets on some nights, and several of the larger boats started
to haul ashore their nets, prior to curing, then overhauling them
ready for the winter's fishing which normally started at the beginning of
November.

One or two of the smaller boats like mine were putting aboard
boulters, that is, a short version of a longline, to catch conger, ling,
ray and dog fish, so I suggested to Lewis we should also haul our nets
ashore and fit ourselves up with a few baskets of line to fill in the gap
until the pilchards came again.

He nearly did a double back somersault when I mentioned a boulter
to him. It soon became obvious that Lewis detested any form of hook
fishing, making it quite clear that he had no intention of ever doing it
again, especially with me, a complete novice. He raised all manner of
objections, painting vivid verbal pictures of me being dragged overboard with the line, or at the very least coming in with several hooks
through interesting parts of my anatomy!

I was equally determined to go boultering, so having tried to reach
some form of agreement, I had to reluctantly suggest that he should
pack up, which he did on the spot, leaving me with a boat full of nets,
no crew and no boulter!

I had become friendly with Roy Cloke, a chap a little younger than myself who had a small tosher in which he went plummeting for mackerel. I had sometimes been out with him on Sunday mornings to learn the ropes and most Saturday nights we went off in my old car for a drink and a bit of crumpet hunting, which was usually much more pleasant than fishing for a living!

Roy and I got on like a house on fire, and I'm pleased to say sixteen years later we still do. His father had some spare tubs of line, so I supplied the boat, Roy the gear, and we split the proceeds down the middle. Roy certainly knew his stuff boultering. When we could not get pilchards for bait we would catch mackerel, shooting on all the inshore patches of rough ground around for miles. We didn't make a lot of money as fish was cheap in those days, but we always managed a fair week's work and the experience I gained proved invaluable in the coming years.

Roy and I also found we could work well together, which we continued to do to our mutual advantage for several years on and off. When the winter pilchard shoals arrived, Roy went in his brother's boat and I shipped another young lad, 'Nipper' Lee with me. Nets were again hauled aboard, but it was soon obvious that the pilchards had not come in any appreciable quantity. Nipper had done a lot of boultering with his father who also had a smallish boat, so he suggested I bought some long line he knew was for sale. This I promptly did.

It was old but serviceable, and as I had acquired more line than two hands could manage comfortably, Nipper introduced me to his mate Albert Morphard, who immediately volunteered to come along with us whenever the lugger he was on was in through lack of pilchards to catch. Albert's skipper was an old man who swore it was better in, looking out, than out looking in, and lived up to this by taking his own advice staying in whenever possible to enjoy the full life! We three lads got on very well from the start. There was much leg pulling and some fruity language at times but we got results, the end produce stuffed into our back pockets on a Saturday morning being our only yardstick of success or failure.

Touch of Bad Weather

My first taste of bad weather was experienced in company with Nipper and Albert. We had shot our bait nets off Looe, catching a couple of baskets of pilchards. While we baited up we discussed where we should shoot and decided to put it away on a smallish bit of ground down the Mevagissey side of Polperro. The shipping forecast that evening had given 0—2 variable, so we were in no hurry, all looking forward to a fine and profitable night. After we had baited four baskets, we decided to shoot that first, then bait up a second four. But the South Easterly motion that had started to roll down made us a bit cautious, so we left the other baiting to see what the weather made first.

The line was duly shot, the kettle boiled, bacon and egg fried and yarns swopped. There was not a breath of wind but more and more swell came rolling in, so after an hour we set to and started to haul. We had plenty of fish right through the line, and a good mixture too.

The most memorable part of the evening came when Albert sank his gaff into a conger of exactly eighty pounds weight! This fish was the largest I have ever caught by any method, although many much larger ones are caught regularly in other parts of the country. Weighing only seven stone himself Albert found the conger was getting the better of him, so with me holding on to his oilskin smock, he gave a mighty heave and managed to get half of the brute in over the rail. The gaff handle snapped off like a carrot, while the conger, never having seen anyone quite like Albert before, decided to return to his abode. As he glided away over the side, Albert grabbed the stump of the gaff with one hand and threw his other arm right round the fish in a violent, slippery embrace.

There was no chance of Albert losing his grip on the great creature, as by this time it had reciprocated by grabbing a great mouthful of the front of his smock. Not wishing to lose either of the two contestants, I pulled them both down onto the stern hatches where quite a tussle ensued until Nipper and I both got gaffs into the brute and dragged it clear of its now quite dishevelled captor! We had quite a ding dong at getting it down into our fish berth while Albert, more indignant than hurt, thank goodness, resumed his position with another gaff to do battle once more.

When we were all in, the wind had freshened from nothing to force six in a matter of two and a half hours, and by the time we had reached Mevagissey an hour and a half later, it had reached near gale force, with the sea cracking right up over the outer harbour walls. So much for the 0—2 variable!

We caught just on ninety stone of fish that night, but had lost a lot of congers through their habit of rubbing their hard serrated jaws across the cotton or hemp stops just behind the hook, which often gave them the chance of breaking free before we could get a gaff into them.

It was after that trip that I decided to try the new number five swivel hooks which several of the larger boats had changed over to, so a basket of new line was made up with three hundred of the new hooks and put aboard with the other eight.

The next trip was to prove beyond all doubt the value of the swivel compared with the old fashioned fixed eye hook. We had bought pilchards for bait and got off just after lunch for grounds South East of the Lizard. It was a very fine day—and it had to be at the time of the year for us to venture so far with a longish line! When we hauled that night we had good fishing right through, and on reaching the basket of line set up with the swivel hooks, which we hauled last, we found what seemed to be a conger on nearly every hook. On our return, we tallied out over two hundred stone and wished we had had all swivel hooks fitted throughout the line. This I was to do for the following spring.

Christmas that year heralded the arrival of a good school of pilchards. So the dahn lines, buffs and creepers were hastily stowed away in the loft together with the line, while our pilchard nets were quickly whipped aboard to give a welcome to the new arrivals!

Chapter 4

Gannets and bubbles

DRIFTING for pilchards in the winter time was a different kettle of fish from the almost genteel occupation it was during the balmy evenings of the summer and autumn. Gales of South or South Westerly wind roared up the channel, often for weeks at a time, occasionally easing for a few hours while the wind came round Nor'West to blow a frizzer, then dappling away before finding its point to blow hard from the Sou'West once more.

Everyone would be mustered ready to go down quay by one-thirty at the latest if the weather was anything like. In those days an almost unlimited supply of pilchards could be handled by the shore side of the industry, as those that were not immediately taken by the canneries were salted down in huge concrete tanks, to be broken out, then pressed and packed in small wooden barrels for the Italian markets. Mevagissey's quays would be packed with boats laying up to four abreast along them. Boats would come from Plymouth and Porthleven, Newlyn, Mousehole and St Ives, to take part in the winter's pilchard fishing.

Mevagissey had the advantage over all these other ports and harbours because it faces East and gets protection from the Western land initially as far as Chapel Point, then from the land running along as far as the Dodman Point, lastly from the Lizard in to Helford, which affords protection from the great Atlantic swells rolling up the Channel uninterrupted outside of this line of land.

As the visiting boats had their crews living aboard they were always the first to put to sea. Fine great luggers they were too, very well founded and well engined for those days. Many of them went long-lining as far as a hundred miles to the West and South West of Newlyn during the spring and summer months, so working from Mevagissey and its sheltered position was really a bit of a holiday for them! Our luggers would be the next to leave, followed by our pint-sized efforts, then if the weather wasn't too bad, by the 'Mosquito fleet'. These were the largest of the toshers, twenty-two to twenty-six feet, mostly completely open, some with a small cuddy and canopy for'ard. They would carry four to six nets. Our craft being a bit larger and considerably safer in bad weather, carried eight to ten nets.

17

The sight of a completely open tosher popping slowly into harbour with six one hundred and twenty yard pilchard nets and 400 stone of pilchards aboard was not one for the faint hearted! The holes where the leg bolts fitted through the topsides of the boat would be plugged from the outside with pieces of headrope cork. Often exhaust outlets would be completely submerged, with the second motor unstartable owing to the back pressure of water in the system.

Many of these smaller boats relied on a hurricane light at mast head with a Tilley storm pressure lantern tied to an upright, when hauling. Later the Board of Trade was to tighten up on regulations governing obligatory lighting and safety equipment generally—not before time I may add. On that point of safety at sea, I feel I should mention the good work done by the meteorological services, especially with forecasts for shipping. These are steadily improving in accuracy and information, but are often ingored completely by many holiday makers and amateur sailors. I get very annoyed when some twit, usually in the summer, says for all to hear—"Bah, they don't know anything about the weather really. All guess work you know. Look at yesterday".

Cornwall is a peninsular, very exposed in most areas, also subject to quick changes and many variations of its weather. No one can give a completely accurate forecast for an area such as ours unless a very stable set of weather conditions exist for the adjoining areas, but the general forecasts are excellent, especially if combined with our own local forecasts and local knowledge. There are times when the weather forecast comes faster than has been anticipated, usually bad weather! On the other hand, it may be diverted or absorbed by other quick changes of pressure and by-pass us completely.

If the beginner makes a habit of listening to the shipping forecasts and also local forecasts, then observing the actual conditions existing in his area at that time, he should soon be able to do his own forecasting, especially if he takes note of conditions existing in adjoining sea areas. Although we are in the Plymouth sea area, we often get a more accurate picture of our area by noting the Lundy area forecast, as it must be remembered the areas forecast are very large, and bound to vary a bit within that area.

So holiday makers and amateurs boating for pleasure, ask, ask, ask! Listen, listen, listen! And if in doubt—don't go out.

Always Take Time to Think

When drift netting, Nipper and I would try to size up the situation and never shoot in a hurry, because once the nets were overboard we were committed, at least for the evening's shoot. The shoals of pilchards would be dived upon by great numbers of gannets—beautiful white diving birds much larger and heavier than the sea gull. If the shoals were well down, the gannets would circle, then fall from hundreds of feet, sending up large plumes of water on impact with the surface. Their momentum coupled with their ability to swim extremely fast underwater, enables them to reach and catch fish a long way beneath the surface, although I cannot say accurately what their limit would be. If the shoals were just under the surface, the gannets would flop in from a few feet, to surface again almost immediately prior to swallowing their catch properly.

In fine weather we often encountered gannets sitting on the water. To find out whether one had been recently feeding on pilchards, we would steer straight for it at the same time shouting and waving for all we were worth. If the bird was full of fish it would have to bring up its stomach contents before being light enough to take off to avoid us, thus giving us a good indication there were pilchards in the immediate area. If it flew straight off, we too just kept going. This trick only worked if there was little or no wind of course.

The great thing before shooting was to decide which way the fish were travelling. Shoals tended to swim to windward on most occasions, and often the last boats to shoot on a large shoal were the most successful.

I remember one afternoon we found a large shoal some way from the rest of the fleet. We had no fish finder, but the number of gannets working was enough sign for us. We lay to and watched points. The stench of pilchard oil filled our nostrils as all manner of fish harried the shoal sending small pieces of the oily fish floating to the surface. Nipper was kneeling down looking over the side near the bows, watching the water.

"Look at the bubbles" he shouted to me, pointing down into the water.

I went up alongside him. Looking down I saw thousands of tiny bubbles sizzling to the surface in long, unbroken lines, as if the sea in that particular spot was fermenting, like home brewed wine in its early stages. The sun was still well up in the sky, and every few moments I could see pilchards rolling and flashing as they caught the light through the stinking green water.

It was obvious we were sitting over a shoal of shoals that sunny winter afternoon. We discovered it was moving at a fair lick to the West'ard and, for once throwing caution to the winds, we motored a good way West side of the shoal, then shot our eight nets.

Nipper had seen many more winters fishing than I had. His main worry was that if the fish hit the nets in too large a quantity, we would not get the far end aboard in time, before the fish died and the nets went down to the bottom by their sheer weight. Even luggers with six men or more aboard often had to cut nets away through being unable to handle them once they had gone down.

We had just set the mizzen and swung the boat head to wind when the fish hit our fleet of nets. Gannets started to pound down onto the nets, so without stopping for our customary cup of tea, we hauled away.

There was no time to shake out. We hauled our whole fleet into the net room; even then, by the time we reached our last two nets, they were on the point of going down. The cobles had already disappeared, only the tops of our large white canvas buffs were visible, just below the surface.

We arrived in quay that afternoon, with four hundred and eighty stone aboard and daylight still in the sky! It was the most pilchards I ever caught in daylight, also the first and only time I was to witness such a shoal of fish that it bubbled, so great was its density and size.

If there was any weather at all, the harbour was the scene of feverish activity all day and night. Boats would be coming in with up to fifteen hundred stone of fish aboard, sometimes even more, often with only part of their fleets unmeshed, the rest run in, laying in great silver piles spilling over from their net rooms. Gangs of men loaded lorry load after lorry load, whilst crews worked on unmeshing, then hauling back, kept going by numerous mugs of tea and the thought that if they eased up they would not be finished in time for the fast approaching next afternoon's fishing.

Everywhere you went in Mevagissey then you could find pilchard scales. In the streets, shops, pubs and homes. It was the sign of prosperity winter time. Alas, there were to be many winters when the pilchards did not come and, even worse for the industry, there came the closure of the canneries and cessation of the salted pilchard trade.

I had taken part in and witnessed the last big winter's pilchard season Mevagissey was to have.

The whole economy of Mevagissey had once relied upon the pilchard, but as young people went into trades ashore rather than follow their parents footsteps, so the average age of the men left increased alarmingly. Even with the continuation of the industry, it was obvious to me that things would alter drastically during the next few years, as young men were taking the easier life, with plenty of time off in the evenings and weekends to spend the money they were earning steadily each week ashore.

Chapter 5

Dick and Roy put me through it!

WE saw the rest of that winter through without mishap and with plenty of fish, carried on through the spring of the following year catching winks. These were pilchards that had just spawned and were thin and terribly feeble. Large, very soft meshed nets had to be used as the fish in that condition simply didn't have the strength to swim and mesh themselves in a tight or hard one. The fish congregated in the bays, turning the water an inky black with their excreta when they were in any quantity. This was the only time of the year this happened and was either caused by the plankton they fed on or by some change in their body chemistry after spawning.

It was just routine work, shooting long fleets of gear, then hauling and shaking the dull, razor-like creatures from our nets. The price wasn't much either, but we caught such large quantities that it made it worthwhile. Winks were of no use for the salting or normal canning trade, as they have little flesh and next to no oil content, but they were canned just the same for export abroad to a country which shall remain nameless. No doubt someone out there made a fat profit from them!

Nipper and I put the line back aboard after the winks finally departed which they had the habit of doing almost overnight.

We carried on until the end of May when he had to join his father aboard the family boat to carry visitors and plummet for mackerel. Albert, who had been our invaluable guest artist for most of that time, had to say farewell also with the coming of the spring pilchards again.

Roy's father, Dick, collared me one Saturday morning, after I had been drying my line on the quay wall prior to curing it.

"How don'ee go spiltering this summer my zun?" he ventured, blowing his cheeks out while he eyed me critically from under the peak of what had once been a cap.

"Too late now, Dick" I replied, "Haven't got any line set up."

Dick grinned like a suntanned toothless Cheshire cat, then solemnly raised the index finger of his right hand to his nose.

"Aaah" he said, then turned away to resume his stance gazing from the cliff wall across the harbour.

I knew, if I waited long enough, a further pronouncement would be forthcoming from him, so I took up position alongside and watched the visitors walk in and out of the quay below us.

"What's it like, fella?". I felt a hand on my shoulder and turned to find Roy had taken up position on my starboard side. He passed a very critical and somewhat rude remark about a fat woman's bottom, a good part of which hung bulging and burnt from what appeared to be shorts.

Dick followed this up with an even wittier remark about her top hamper, while I, having only her face or legs to comment on, refrained from further remarks and suggested we adjourned to The Fountain, a short distance down the street, for a drink.

"'Ang on a minute 'fore we go" said Dick, "tell Stan what we got in mind mate".

Roy, always a little shy, looked across the harbour, then turned looking very seriously at me.

"Father's got some spilter, good lines, too. What about if we come with you for the summer?"

"Suits me", I replied.

"Aaah! Done!" said Dick.

It was settled, so we adjourned to The Fountain to discuss details. By eight the following morning they had the baskets of spilter aboard complete with four old galvanised wash tubs. They had also brought over a box of mackerel and a large case of rock salt from the fish store to whom I landed. I was told to get the dahn lines, buffs, creepers etc. down from the loft and not to hang about! On my return I was surprised to find they had not only cut up the bait but were well through baiting up one of the baskets.

"Come on my zun, you 'ave this wan we've started, ten a minute mind, and don'ee look around at the red lips!"

I could see baiting a spilter would not allow much time for gazing up at the assorted "Birds" who peered inquisitively down upon us from the edge of the quay, but ten hooks a minute was surely pushing things!

I wisely made no comment, and after Roy had shown me the right way to put the little pieces of salted mackerel on the fine wire hooks, then sprinkle them with salt as they laid around the outside edges of tub, with the line and stops neatly coiled in the centre, I got stuck in, head down and no messing.

I thought I was doing well, I'd show them how to bait hooks, after all I was quite fast with a longline.

After a while Roy said, "Come on old man—most time to 'ave wan".

I turned to see that he and Dick had both finished their baths whilst

I had quite a way to go, even with the advantage of half a tub's start.

Much deflated, I returned to my task . . . what little zip I had started with had vanished, I was down to about three hooks a minute, let alone ten! My mates each lit a Woodbine, then gave me a hand to finish off.

We had plenty of fuel aboard, so all that there remained to do was to put the boat in the outer harbour ready for the following morning, as 3 a.m. would be around low water time.

Before parting our separate ways, I was given strict instructions not to oversleep even if I had to sit up all night! The irony was that when we mustered next morning, there was a fine breeze of south west wind and we all trapsed off back to bed again.

Later that morning I had several enquiries directed at me as to why I wasn't out, but by then I had learned the finer points of thrust and counter thrust needed to survive verbal combat with those who populated the quays. Some remarks I either ignored, replied to sensibly or parried with a quick retort laced with heavy sarcasm, depending on who had originated the query.

By this time in my short fishing career I had had a row with everyone without exception, down the harbour, but I was also in the unique position of being a complete outsider, unrelated to everyone and, bearing no malice, I spoke to all and sundry regardless of any differences of opinion.

It seemed most of the chaps carried family grudges to an extreme, many families never speaking to others at all, so my social life was very uncomplicated compared with most.

Off on Spiltering Trip

By Tuesday, the weather had fined off and we had a gift of a morning for our first spiltering trip together. Dick gave me the time to travel and course to follow. One hour and twenty minutes S.S.E. by E. from Chapel Point. I drank tea and steered off as Dick and Roy baited up the spare bath with fresh mackerel. This was to be shot last and reckoned to catch more whiting than the salted bait. The wisdom of salting the baits in the other baths of line was evident when we had stayed in for bad weather the day before.

Daylight was forming as I stopped off the main engine. By this time Dick and Roy had finished the baiting and also had cut up and salted the rest of the mackerel we had brought with us. The dahn and buff were thrown away, then the dahn line streamed off, eighty fathoms of six thread manilla to which was attached the creeper which is a light, five clawed anchor.

The top of the first tub of line was then bent into the other end of the creeper and shooting commenced.

It was, in fact, exactly the same procedure as longlining with the exception that the lines and hooks were much smaller. I steered the boat in shooting on the same course as we had come off, to enable the line to lay across the tide as much as possible yet still be shot with it. The flood tide was running from west to east and vice versa when on the ebb.

Dick shot the line like a man with the devil after him. It had already been wetted by pouring a few buckets of water through it to stop it sticking together as it was being thrown. The water drained away again through holes punched in the bottoms of the baths expressly for this purpose. Roy knelt by the bath, turning it, also clearing any hooks that looked likely to cause trouble.

The only directions I got from Dick as he warmed to his task were "Put 'er on—bit more, in on, my zun, give it to 'er".

Once we were all out, I changed ends while Roy boiled the kettle. Dick was already eating one half of a truly enormous cold pasty, which he washed down with about three large mugs of tea.

I later found he loved great quantities of salt with his food and this required large amounts of tea to slake his thirst, which in turn gave him violent indigestion! He consumed a large supply of patent indigestion tablets day and night, and these also required washing down with adequate quantities of tea as the peppermint also made him thirsty. What a man! The only time he ever wore his teeth was the day he left the dentist after collecting them, and this too must have added to the misery he and his stomach constantly endured.

The First Haul
Being fine and sunny, also by this time, knowing my way about a bit better, I had no difficulty in finding the inside dahn. We had a good length of line out, 2800 hooks at four foot six inches apart. Roy had first haul.

As soon as the first part of the line came in, Dick unbent it, then started to rebait, making sure of removing all particles of old bait from the hooks in case they turned the new baits sour. A few whiting, gurnards and rough dogs kept coming up, but nothing startling.

Dick took over on the second bath while I was passed back the one Dick had started baiting to carry on with.

As soon as part of the next one came in Roy did as Dick had done and starting baiting that. It being fine, I managed to bait away, whilst attending to the boat, knocking the engine in and out of gear as commanded by the person hauling, and keeping her nearly head into the tide to facilitate recovering the line properly.

Dick started unhooking a few larger whiting—"Aaah, red fins!" he exclaimed, holding out a thumping great reddish finned whiting. "More 'ere zum wheres when you see that'."

Sure enough, a few minutes later, Dick turned to me. With raised fingers and his inimitable toothless grin, he growled "My Goor—I got 'un down 'ere, wan on every 'ook my zun!"

Although prone to considerable exaggeration at times, Dick proved to be right. Looking down the line as far as I could see there was a large whiting on every hook.

The spot reached through to the end of Dick's tub, then when my turn came to haul, fishing turned patchy again. I did manage one large hake, which I rubbed into the others a bit to console myself on my seeming inability to pull in a decent splat of whiting.

When we came to the spare line which had the fresh bait on it, there was no splat of fish but good fishing from end to end, which proved its value as an extra, to be baited and shot when the weather was moderate enough.

I did let the side down, though, that day through my inexperience. Roy was hauling and shouted "Gaff!" I had it ready, immediately gaffing the first of two turbot as they reached the surface.

"Not that one you daft . . . . . . r! The one underneath! Oh my Goor!"

Yes, I had gaffed the fish that was already hooked! The other swam off.

I was often to see two turbot come up together after that, one hooked, the other swimming by its side unable to understand what had happened to its mate, but I never made that mistake again. I had my leg pulled about that for years afterwards.

All the way back home it was baiting up for us. We landed over seventy stone of whiting, then went to lunch. As soon as that was over, back to finish off, after which I crept back home for a nap until tea time.

I had a pint with Roy afterwards, but was too tired to even play a game of darts, creeping off to bed again sharp at nine.

As spilter line was much finer than long line, my hands were raw from hauling it. My left thumb was shredded where I had unwittingly put it in the gills of the fish to get a better grip whilst unhooking it. My index and adjoining fingers on my left hand were riddled with hook pricks due to baiting operations, while the backs of my hands were skinned where rough dogs had scruffed me as I had taken them off. They were of no commercial value, but we unhooked most of them properly to avoid breaking the stops which often happens if we strapped them over the rail too hard to render them completely unconscious!

I later learned that by soaking my hands in warm water and Dettol great relief could be obtained. It also prevented cuts etc. turning septic in quantity, but constant use of the spilter was the only real cure for the agony I endured in those first few days.

Needless to say, I was glad when Friday lunchtime came. We let the rest of the baiting go until the following morning, squaring up bills and going sharing before having a well-earned drink before lunch.

It was never easy, spiltering. I mastered it thanks to Dick and Roy, whose good humour, patience and know-how made it possible. It was always worth it though, especially when you could look down in the water and see "Wan on every hook, by Goor!"

Chapter 6

I get hooked properly

Roy and I spent most of our spare time together, having a drink and playing darts, a game we were quite dab hands at. One Saturday evening, in the late autumn, we were having a good evening in a pub at Par, a small village and port just off St Blazey. I was very attracted by a young lady who was having a drink with several of her friends. There was a small dance hall over the licensed premises and they had come down during one of the intervals. I mentioned I liked the look of her, and to my surprise Roy informed me he knew her.

"Come on, mate, introduce us" I says, which he promptly did. It transpired the young lady in question had worked in Mevagissey at the pilchard cannery for some time prior to me moving to the village, and she lived at St Blazey with her parents.

A few weeks later, we met again and after a lot of persuasion she agreed to come out with me for an evening. Hilda Mary Bonney instinctively distrusted me at first sight, I cannot think why! Anyway, she eventually found I wasn't quite as crafty or lecherous as my appearance suggested, and we were going steady by the following spring. I nicknamed Hilda "Bonny" because she always looked it. Although it was also the way her surname was pronounced, to me it was the most natural name to call her, she did not object to this, so the name stuck.

I had shipped a chap called John Pennell with me after the summer's spilter season. John had never done any fishing before, but worked hard. Although plagued by sea sickness, he stayed with me for a couple of years until we had a disagreement in the May prior to my marriage on the 14th June that year. John never really came to terms with sea, but he was the hardest worker I ever had with me, never shirking jobs ashore and in the loft which was something many other so called fishermen did, to the overall detriment of their livelihoods.

I had built a wheelhouse on the *Joyance* whilst John had been with me and when he left I decided to clean and paint the boat really properly then licence her for carrying passengers during the coming summer months.

By the middle of June I was well and truly hooked! Bonny and I had a few days honeymoon, staying at her parents home whilst we travelled around enjoying the beautiful weather and each other's company. Then it was back to live with my parents for a spell until we could get a place of our own.

Trips for an hour

I had licensed the boat and been granted a boatman's licence, so on returning from honeymoon I started an apprenticeship harder than any fishing I had or was ever likely to do. On my notice board prominently displayed from the wheelhouse roof, it stated I was licensed to carry twelve passengers for fishing and pleasure. But when I was issued with my boatman's licence, they didn't tell me I would be engaged in open warfare with over thirty other gentlemen of fortune like myself, whose ages ranged from thirty to seventy-eight; and the older they were the tougher and more cantankerous they got.

Before the visitors thickened up in July and August, we would all go mackereling from dawn until around eight or just after, then we would land, wash down the boat thoroughly and nip home for a quick breakfast. On returning there would be long heated arguments as to who was in before someone else. Our excellent harbour master, Mr Winston Baron would keep discreetly out of the way, unless called in to adjudicate, as he was certain to seriously upset one of the contestants, thereby being ostracized for the rest of the year by the loser, although his decisions were always scrupulously fair to all concerned.

By the end of the first month of my new occupation, I had been cursed, sworn at, challenged to several fights (one by a man of seventy-two) and had had my life generally made so miserable I seriously contemplated scrubbing the rest of the season and getting back to fishing again.

However, I like a challenge and I gave myself a good talking to and set about analysing the problem properly. As I had the largest boat engaged in running trippers, I reasoned that I stood a fair chance of filling up fairly quickly, right out off the end steps of the lighthouse quay.

Like fishing though, bait was needed. I knew that visitors, like whiting, went for mackerel, so every morning I would keep a dozen or so back from my catch, to sit idly filleting them as I lay moored at the steps waiting for a bite! It worked like magic!

"Did you catch those mackerel this morning? Will you sell us some?"

"Do you always fillet mackerel like that?"

"Why not come out and catch your own?" I would reply, knowing that if I left the filleting of the fish they would catch until I got back in again, it would create enough interest from the onlookers to virtually guarantee another load, who would eagerly nip aboard for an hours

trip with a few mackerel ready for the pan chucked in for good measure
—and all for half a crown!

Alas, I did too well. By August, there was such resentment from
the others, that several of them got together and suggested to the
harbour master that all boats should run on a rota system unless
previously booked. Names were to be drawn out of a hat at 9 a.m.
every morning. Each boat was to take its turn accordingly, no boat
going out a second time until all the boats running that day had done
their first trip, unless privately booked.

Most of the boatmen were all for the new scheme, with the exception
of those who had largish, clean boats. These were doing well enough
as they were, but the majority carried the day, unable to see the time
that would be wasted by all having to be in at 9 every morning, and
the money most of them would lose operating the new scheme.

I suggested that the draw should be done for the whole week at one
go, so everyone knew in advance where they stood, but several thought
I had an ulterior motive in suggesting such a course and my suggestion
was unanimously turned down until a few years later, when many of
the older diehards had retired or been refused licenses owing to their
senility.

Most of the older men, especially those with dirty, ill equipped
boats, supported the scheme wholeheartedly at its inception. No
wonder! Several of the old perishers were lucky to get a couple of
trips in a day, while the more pleasant chaps with cleaner, larger
boats, could do six or more on a good day. Often we would have to
wait behind one of the worst-kept boats for an hour or more, until
in desperation a crowd would go aboard and he would clear off.

I finished that season a lot wiser and a bit better off. I reasoned
there must be a better way of making money out of the throngs of
visitors who visited Mevagissey in summer time, without quarrelling
and bickering solidly for four or five months, but the answer eluded
me for a further two years.

Two Great Characters

That winter a great character shipped with me for the pilchard
season. There were, in fact, two of them—Russell Blamey and Rover
his mongrel dog and inseperable companion. Russell had bright red
hair, Rover's was reddish brown! Russell argued with everyone around
the quay incessantly, whilst Rover 'saw off' every dog that dared to
put his nose around either of the approaches to the harbour. I was
always glad they were on my side!

Rover sailed with us regularly, unless he went courting, then business
had to come before pleasure, or was it the other way around? He
would jump or be carried aboard to curl up and sleep in the wheel-

house until we had shot our nets and brewed up. Then he would wake up, as if by magic, and join us in for'ard for a few tit bits and his saucer of tea. While we hauled, he would stand for'side of Russell, occasionally snapping at the gulls as they flew past in their efforts to denude our nets of fish as they came in over the roller. When we were all in, he would quietly return to his corner in the wheelhouse and go off to sleep again.

The thing that intrigued me about Rover was that no matter what direction we came in from, or how long it took us, he would not stir until we were about half a mile from the harbour; then, as if awakened by someone, he would get up, stretch, then walk up for'ard to stand like a statue in the bows, front feet on the rail until we passed in through the quay heads. When there was a thick fog, either day or night, his behaviour was exactly the same; he came out of the wheelhouse only when we were half a mile or less from the harbour. If we made landfall some way to the West'ard, then eased down to motor along shore until around the head, he would remain curled up, unperturbed. Strange, but perfectly true.

Russell, I'm glad to say, is very well, though only doing a bit of summer boating nowadays, but Rover, poor fellow, died several years ago.

Chapter 7

I join the mosquito fleet

THE pilchard season Russell and Rover had shared with me was mainly a failure, as were those to come in the future.

I worked the *Joyance* mostly single handed during the following year, with the exception of a few long line trips in the early summer.

It was on the last trip of this series that the old Britt motor I have already described in detail, undoubtedly saved my life. I was three handed—an old hand Dick Behennah, and a youngster from London, Tony Wood, whom I had shipped on to try out, as he had pestered me for so long prior to this. It was his first and last trip.

We shot our bait nets in the bay, waiting until eleven that evening before enough pilcahrds had drained in for our needs. We left at midnight, motoring until seven the next morning before shooting as we had to motor to the south'ard of other Mevagissey boats to get a clear berth. Although fine at the time, it was obvious that the weather was breaking up fast. We changed ends to haul with the ebb, and when we had nearly reached the dahn we saw a French crabber obviously working away in the distance at our other end!

Back we went again, the Frenchman waited until we had nearly reached them, then they jettisoned our line, creeper dahn etc. in a heap before motoring off like a torpedo boat. That wasted a further hour of what was to be valuable time.

Dick and I worked as fast as we could, but were hampered by heavy fishing, there being many spur dogs and rays on the line. Our third hand had collapsed with sea sickness in the early hours of the morning, and was wedged in a corner of the cuddy by life jackets to stop him rolling about. He did not rise again until we hauled him out and hoisted him ashore the following evening.

We managed to get underway by midday with a fast freshening Southerly wind on our starboard quarter. Four hours later we were running before a full gale; rain lashed down in solid sheets almost horizontally with visibility almost nil. I was extremely frightened and expected every huge sea that towered up to be the one to overwhelm us. But our time had not come, and I managed more by luck than judgement to keep our "bit of wood" running even on the big ones when they broke.

After we had been motoring for six hours, the main engine started to run very roughly, so I eased it down to half throttle. It ran falteringly for a further quarter of an hour, then ground to a stop.

I was later to find that it had run and finally seized up its fore-end bearing, but under the prevailing conditions I had no chance even to try to start it again, let alone examine it.

With the old Britt flat out I did not have the speed to do anything other than run dead before the sea and wind. Before this I had been edging her in on our course at every opportunity the seas gave me. Now we started taking in seas over the stern, but somehow we managed to clear one lot before the next one came in. Our luck was holding, but I felt I could never keep in far enough to make the shelter of the bay, as I had purposely run up a deep course to avoid an error and subsequently running against a lee shore.

As if suddenly turned off, the wind died down. A few minutes later it came again, this time from the North West. The rain stopped, the sky lifted and there Nor'West by West of us, lay Mevagissey. We were still about four miles off, but now with our mizzen up to steady us, we came up head to wind and slowly made ground towards home. The Nor'West wind came off a frizzer and we shipped water over the bows, over the port side—and sometimes we rolled to starboard and the damned stuff jumped in that way too, but I no longer cared.

Dick took the wheel and I pumped. The sight of home gave me renewed energy. My oilskin hat had caught the wind from behind and departed some time in the afternoon. Sweating profusely, I had torn my scarf away from my neck, and now was taking a steady stream of water down the neck of my smock. It was a long time before I realised that I was completely wet through, even my sea boots were full, so I tore them off and stood cheerfully pumping in my bare feet, one of the happiest men at sea anywhere in the world that late afternoon!

The old Britt cuffed away, never faltering, every minute making better weather for us as we slowly neared the land, and at eight o'clock we made harbour—too late to land our catch, but very thankful to be alive.

In landing my fish the following morning, I was told that we should have been in earlier the evening before, so we received very poor prices for a catch of two hundred stone, eighty of which had been prime blond and thornback rays.

Of course, it was immediately iced and packed ready for despatch the next day, to make as good a price as it would have done at any other time, but there was no use remonstrating with them.

I never went lining in the *Joyance* again after the way I was treated by that buyer, but I was able to put the memory and experience of it to good use a few years later, when I was a founder member of The Fishermen's Cooperative here at Mevagissey. I ran visitors for the rest of the summer and autumn doing as many angling trips as I could rather than spend fruitless hours queuing up at steps and the slipway.

As I did not wish to spend the winter waiting for fish to come, I decided to get a job in the cannery, then advertise the *Joyance* and buy a smaller boat with part of the proceeds. Bonney and I had been blessed with our daughter, Carol, who was then seven months old and although the money at the factory was not brilliant, every little helped.

I spent the following winter helping to cook and can frozen Japanese tuna, not bad for a pilchard cannery in Cornwall. In between lorry loads of tuna we had even more lorry loads of carrots, which were sliced and also canned. Just for good measure we had an occasional load of pilchards in, which also needed canning.

The organised chaos created by the different operations with the limited staff and equipment available, was something to behold. I managed to do three jobs at a time when we were canning carrots, and there were some enthusiastic souls who did so many different operations during the course of a day, that had they stopped to think what they were doing, they would have collapsed with the mental strain.

The manager was a great character. Small and athletic, he would sprint around the premises like a boxer doing his roadwork, getting everybody working faster and faster. If a machine slowed up or stopped, he would appear as if by magic a few seconds later, to ask why or hurl himself frenziedly into the task of repairing it. Always neatly dressed and sporting an immaculate white linen coat, he nearly always managed to stay spotlessly clean, a thing I was never able to do for more than ten minutes or so at the start of a day.

One day a very old pilchard canning machine refused service. There were a pair of these mechanical monstrosities at one end of the ground floor. They stood, there, mechanical relics of an age long since past, driven by chains, sprockets, cams, levers and—would you believe it—rubber bands? All the oval tins turned out from the cannery went through these horrible contraptions, for sealing, leaving them festooned and dripping with a mixture of lubricating oil and tomato puree after operating for an hour or so.

The manager fiddled and jiggered around for a spell, then started the machine to try it. A few tins went through, but they were not sealed properly so further adjustments were made which resulted in his white coat becoming well spattered in black oil. I watched him becoming more and more irritated—I was quite pleased to see him getting dirty for once in his spotlessly clean existence. He started the machine again, bending down to watch the rollers run around the edges of the tins as they went through for sealing.

The adjustments gave the machine a marvellous opportunity to do what many of the employees had secretly dreamed of for years. With a steady clanking and screeching, it hurled tin after tin of partially cooked pilchards and puree back the way they were going in, splattering the manager liberally over his face and chest, and finished the job with a large dollop on the back of his head as he turned to avoid further punishment! The foreman turned the machine off, trying hard to look sympathetically at the splattered form that had appeared to help him a few minutes before.

It was too much for either of them. The foreman turned away to stifle a screaming laugh with a fit of coughing; the manager shot off to his adjoining cottage for a good wash and change. I did enjoy that!

I was able to sell the *Joyance* that winter, getting my asking price. Then I bought a twenty foot tosher I had had my eyes on for some time previously.

Back to Fish Again

As soon as a reasonable quantity of pilchards arrived in the early spring, I left the cannery to go aboard a lugger drifting, on the understanding that I would leave again as soon as the mackerel arrived around April or May so that I could work my recently acquired boat. The mackerel arrived on time so I started off on another localised form of fishing, plummetting for mackerel.

Most everyone coming to Mevagissey on holiday has had a few trips around the bay in a tosher, hauling in the mackerel lines whilst shouting or squeeling with excitement as they find they have caught one of the streamlined, beautifully marked fish. However, very few people realise what a skilled job plummetting for mackerel is.

With the introduction of the mackerel feathers to Cornwall a few years ago, plummetting has now been superseded, but for many years it provided fisherman with a good living, whilst other methods of fishing sometimes yielded hardly any income at all.

A plummet was always moulded locally in lead. It consisted of a flat bottomed cone weighing from two and a half to three pounds, straighter on one side than the other. An arm of tarred hemp or cotton line was pushed through a hole nearly at the top, then made fast with a small towing eye, which was spliced in, then pulled back until it jammed in the hole solidly. The eye protruded on the straighter edge of the lead, while a seven to eight inch arm stuck out opposite—the stiffer the arm the better, hence the tar.

Two tapered wooden booms were fixed one each side of the boat. The lines were towed from the ends of these and also fixed to tripping lines attached to each quarter for keeping them straight—also of course for hauling them aboard. The third line was attached to the stern. On this one, four fathoms were allowed from the surface to the lead, while the quarter lines were half a fathom shorter. The lines were always of fine hemp or white cotton. Half a fathom of fine line was also attached to each plummets' arm, then a largish swivel and another two fathoms of twelve to sixteen pound breaking strain nylon, while at last came the spinner and hook.

The latter were always tied by the fishermen themselves, the hook and blade being whipped carefully onto very heavy nylon with waxed thread. Treble hooks or single hooks and spinners manufactured by various firms were found to be next to useless for this type of commercial spinning as neither attracted the mackerel like the locally made spinner. Also they were designed badly, being mostly too rigid to enable the fishermen to unhook his fish fast enough. When the first three mackerel of the day were caught, a piece of tail skin would be cut off each, then the spinner hook would be pushed through the very gristly end right up by the tail, the snaid as it was called, being laid skin down on a piece of cork to facilitate pushing the hook point and barb right through it without tearing or squashing it!

The art of plummetting was not so much catching mackerel when they were feeding, which most anybody can do, but to find the mackerel and then encourage them to feed when they were not doing so. When fish were scarce at certain times of the year, the price would be consequently higher, and the skilled plummetter could always make a good living whilst others could only stand and watch him land.

When a mackerel was felt to take the stern line, usually the first to be taken, it being the longest of the three, the boat would be wheeled to starboard in a fairly tight circle, while the starboard and then the stern line were cleared alternately of fish. The port line, with its mackerel left on, would be used as a teaser, which while fresh and swimming naturally the other mackerel never failed to chase.

A good catch depended on many factors. The speed of the boat, whether leeway was counteracted whilst wheeling, the speed of the fisherman unhooking his fish, fast or slowly depending on how they were feeding, and of course, local knowledge of grounds, tides, also considerable knowledge of the mackerel's habits generally.

On hot, calm days, mackerel can only be induced to feed by certain ruses which may seem strange to a newcomer to the job. One was to slow the boat right down, then haul up the stern line only, to lower it again; then repeating the operation with one of the quarter lines. If this failed to stir up the fish's appetites, the stern line would again be raised and lowered, at the same time sharply moving the rudder to one side, then the other, thus creating clouds of bubbles which would generally create enough interest to get the lurking fish up near enough for them to be tempted by the snaided spinners. Heavy leads with long lines were used to start the season with, but these were changed to lighter leads with shorter lines as the season progressed.

The Vagaries of Visitors

As you may have gathered, a boatload of visitors was not conducive to a chap plummetting at his best form! Very often, all three lines would be out of the water at once, with the result that the mackerel, having nothing to follow, soon disappeared again. If the boatman started wheeling, the inside lead would invariably be thrown by some excited passenger right by the edge of the boat, to go straight back and tangle with the stern line. If help were offered them, to throw it in properly, you immediately appeared to condemn them as idiots and were told they could do it very well themselves, thank you!

The drill would, therefore, be a few mackerel and straight out, straight back. The boatman had his fare and the passengers some mackerel.

Most boatmen try to catch as many mackerel as they can for their people especially at times when they are scarce, but when fish is plentiful there is always the crafty chap who steers away from the shoals, loses no leads has no tangles to cut away, and returns with a lovely clean boat at the end of an hour.

I did fairly well plummetting that season. Roy had a boat similar to mine, and I followed him around quite a lot until I got the hang of things. He gave me a lot of good advice and never failed to top my catch, however many I caught. He certainly was one of the smartest mackerel men in the place and only ran a few people if the mackerel went scarce in July and August.

I had my share of trippers and did quite a lot of angling trips mornings and evenings. I had built a canopy for'ard, which afforded my passengers protection from the weather, especially if anchored head to wind with the mizzen sail up. This shelter was to become invaluable later that year, when Roy and I went boultering again.

Bonny and I had been fortunate to rent a very old cottage in the Lily Court, a stone's throw from the western corner of the inner harbour, where my tosher was moored. We had one living room cum kitchen, downstairs, with three bedrooms above, one on top of the other. We did in fact nickname our new abode "The Lighthouse".

In the back wall of the second bedroom up were two doors, one behind the other, the thickness of the wall apart. Through these we could walk out onto a field. If there was not enough wind to dry our clothes in the courtyard below, Bonny would take them up three flights of stairs to our back entrance, where we had a clothes line rigged amongst the buttercups and bullocks!

We shared a 'privy' situated across the yard with our neighbours Barbara and Fred Cloke. Our only source of water was also obtained from the tap in there, so very often one of us needed a bucket of water while the other was in residence, and vice versa. We each had a washing machine. On wash days the drill would be to make sure all duties had been performed by the other parties, then a hose was run out and fixed onto the tap to fill the machine up. Sometimes the flow of water arriving in the washer would dwindle; then a quick sprint was needed to the toilet in order to refit the connection back onto the tap. This operation was invariably accompanied with a cold shower for the operator!

The dirty water from the machine had to be piped out again into the W.C. which was the only outlet for waste water our two families had. The cistern leaked, necessitating sitting well for'ard on the seat; the roof leaked when it rained, and the tap dripped. Being lower than the surrounding courtyard the floor collected a substantial amount of surface water, which seeped away slowly through the cracked cement floor. No wonder we called it "the bog". Ours was the original one I think!

Although the house was old and in a bad state of repair, we all thrived during our time at the Lily Court. The four cottages were eventually condemned and sometime after we had been rehoused on a small council estate newly built at the edge of the village, the whole block collapsed one night as if tired of standing empty in the lonely courtyard.

A Good Season Boultering

That autumn Roy and I put line aboard my boat. It turned out a very good season for us, as we were the only ones boultering at that time. Most of our catch was conger eel, caught along the shore, but now and then, if conditions were right, we would nip off further afield to catch a mixture of fish, which would make more money, especially in times of scarcity during the winter months, although we never received anything like the true value for the fish in those days.

One trip I remember well, as it was a fisherman's dream come true. We had baited up four baskets of line, three hundred swivel hooks in each, with waste pilchard heads from the cannery. We left early, bound for ground off Falmouth, but when we had got past the Dodman Point, we decided not to go so far, as there was a lot of motion in the water with sky building up from the South'ard. We suspected a Southerly blow, so decided to shoot on the very rough ground off the Dodman. We had some average catches there previously, forty to sixty stone a shoot, so whacked the line away, then had our tea.

The weather was still fine when we started to haul, and a good job it stayed that way for a further hour or two. Roy had first pull.

When the creeper jumped clear of the rock, he turned to me just as his Father used to. "I gott'n down year old man—coor—solid", he growled. He had too.

There was just one conger eel after another. The first basket yielded around forty stone, the second one more.

I was fortunate to have a small Coventry Victor diesel engine with a flywheel enclosed in the crank casing which we used as a working motor, for by the time the third basket was aboard, the bulkhead, carlings and hatches had all collapsed under the weight of fish while the boat became one large fishberth! Roy hauled the last of the line standing in a cane fish basket to stop the congers biting his feet.

When he had finished, they were nearly level with the rail, while I was gaffing as many congers going out over the side as Roy was hauling in.

We plugged the leg holes, pumped out, then gaffed several dozen congers from amongst the engines before we got underway. I had a small petrol engine to help drive her. Fortunately this was up clear of the fish, but by the time we got back, the congers had found their own level, like water, and had started to pop up with gay abandon through the stern hatches! We covered the writhing mass with a canvas cover and our sail; put the line baskets, loose hatches etc. on the top, and went home well satisfied with our evening's work; we left the boat anchored in the outer harbour, as it was then low water.

When we walked out quay to unload the following morning, we were met by a fisherman coming in. "You'd better see to your boat Stan, she looks half full of water". It was lovely to be able to tell him the boat was down bends with fish. We unloaded one hundred and seventy stone of large conger, four stone of medium and small, we estimated we lost a further twenty stone out of the boat, for once they get their tail over a rail, they've gone unless you're very quick to stop them. We never bettered that trip in a twenty foot boat.

Chapter 8

A-sharking we will go!

IT was while working with Roy that winter that I met Jack and Babs Cleaver. Jack was a lot older than Babs and had spent most of his time in Canada and the United States in the film industry. Coming to England during the last war, he had met and married Babs. Jack had moved to Mevagissey in semi-retirement with Babs and their two young boys, the previous summer. They were wonderful company. Jack had certainly been around in his time, and could talk for hours about his experiences without ever boring us. Sometimes a film he had been in, was shown on television and we would all sit watching it, pulling his leg something awful! Although well over sixty, Jack had the stature and looks of a man many years younger.

"I want to do a bit of fishing or something" he would say.

"Yes, for heaven's sake get the old chap out of my way doing something Stan" Babs would reply.

After a while I hit upon quite a good idea.

"If you and Babs like to buy a boat I know is for sale here, I'll run it shark fishing next summer, while you advertise it from your bungalow and Jack can do his stuff around the quay as well. He can come out when he wants to and we'll split fifty fifty after expenses", I suggested.

They liked the idea and the *Our John* a twenty-seven foot boat was duly purchased for a very modest sum. Jack bought two harnesses, reels and shark rods, then we made and installed a centre seat for an angler to play his fish from. I painted a large notice board which we hung from their bungalow garden. This commanded everyone's attention who came in and out on the main road through to the harbour. Several small advertisements were also popped into angling papers. The stage was set, now all we needed were the customers.

I was busy running trippers in my boat during the week that followed. The weather was fine with light westerly winds. Jack appeared above me on the quay while I was awaiting my turn for a Friday evening trip.

"I've got three for tomorrow Stan", he said. So we had finally got some customers. I confirmed I would be ready to go at nine the following morning. Jack had certainly tried hard enough, chatting up people all around the harbour. I had insisted that Jack should get a pound deposit for each prospective sharker, to be returned if we could not sail owing to weather or a breakdown; and if the angler was unable to come on an alternative day.

Next morning dawned fine. Our three customers arrived with Jack bang on time, so I was able to get out on the shark grounds by eleven thirty. I stopped off the engines, then filled two fine net bags with pilchard offal and hung one for'ard, one aft on the windward side of the boat. As the boat rolled the bags flopped up and down in the water releasing a trail of "Rubby Dubby" which we hoped would attract at least one shark. The mizzen sail was hoisted, then eased so that we sat slightly up into the wind and motion while we drifted at a fair speed to lee.

After baiting the single hooks with small whole mackerel, the floats were set, then the lines run out.

The sharkers tossed a coin for first turns, harnesses were put on, then we explained what would happen when they had a run, also how the big Penn multiplying reels worked.

I had taken a crowd of London chaps sharking a few times several years prior to this, so knew a bit about it. They always had their own gear, of a sort, but caught sharks and handled them extremely well without the aid of a harness or modern more sophisticated reels. Shark fishing had really caught on at Looe, a beautiful fishing village situated on a river between Mevagissey and Plymouth, so we were now using gear which had more or less become standardised. The rods were fibreglass, not too heavy but strong enough to take a good bashing if needed.

An American Penn 9/0 multiplying reel was used, loaded to capacity with eighty pounds breaking strain braided nylon line terminating in a fourteen foot wire trace, a lead, two large swivels and a stout hook. The floats were two herring net corks tied together with the line passed through the hole in the middle; the bait was set at the required depth by jamming the line through a knife cut in the cork. It was found best to set one bait at eight to twelve fathoms, one at three, the deeper line being the for'ard one, which was allowed to run out to about twenty-five yards from the boat, the shallow line aft being kept close by. Over a season the differently set lines would take about the same amount of fish, and of course by using the method described we generally stopped a shark from taking two hooks at once, as well as the ensuing arguments as to who had hooked it first!

Shark Hooked!

Well, back on board the *Our John*, things were pretty quiet. Our customers had long since finished cracking jokes about sharks and what they would do if they caught one. Jack was doing a crossword while I kept the rubby bags full and watched the floats.

Zzzzzzz—the reel on the for'ard rod screamed as a shark ran nearly a hundred yards of line from it. Our three customers all tried to sit in the fighting seat together, while I tried to give the rod to the chap on turn.

The fish made his second run while I was still sorting things out. The angler struck his fish correctly, and it fought well for several minutes before I was able to gaff it aboard and clobber it.

We saw it was a small male blue shark. We had the run at 2 p.m. which turned out to be the only one of the day. What a difference old Johnny shark made! One minute our three passengers were laying around fed up to their teeth, the next the boat was alive with figures leaping around with cameras, their shouts and laughter continuing for some time after the catch had been brought aboard.

On arriving in quay, we laid alongside while Jack hoisted the fish and scales up the mast to weigh it. It was only 48 lbs, but the interest it created hanging up there with the scale hook through its top jaw prominently displaying a row of razor sharp pointed teeth, was to be worth more than that in pounds sterling.

We did not get a trip the next day in spite of the large crowd that had gathered on the quay to see the shark. We had the boat booked for the Sunday by a friend of mine, a publican and his mates from St Blazey—Bonney's home town, and this was to be our next trip.

A fine hot windless day produced three large blue female sharks between 70 to 90 lbs. These broke the ice for us as far as bookings were concerned. From then on we worked steadily through until the end of that September.

Two Sharks a Day

During the next winter the wing motor was overhauled and a secondhand 22 h.p. Kelvin diesel was purchased to replace the old poppet type petrol/paraffin main engine, which I swear was only held together by thick rust, paint and carbon deposits! A canopy had already been built and fitted on during the actual season, so the following year we were far more organised.

Bookings started to come in during April and May, and apart from the weather at times, we had very few days in, averaging just over two sharks a day for eighty-four trips.

Tim Wright, a young chap from Kingston, Surrey, came down for a week's shark fishing that year. The weather had been nasty during his stay, but he achieved his ambition which was to qualify for membership in the Shark Angling Club of Great Britain, by catching a shark of over 75 lbs.

Later that autumn, Tim's mother and father came down and had
several days angling with us, which they both thoroughly enjoyed.
It was a pleasure taking the Wright family out, as they were all fond
of the sea and also were very good anglers. Tim's father, Bill Wright,
had retired from the pressures of big business earlier that year. His
health was not too good at that time, so he contemplated moving
down to Mevagissey to recuperate, and to fill in part of his new found
leisure, angling.

At the end of our second shark season, Mr and Mrs Wright had
bought the *Our John* from Jack and Babs, also their bungalow in
Valley Road. Tim was finishing at university that winter, so intended
joining his parents at Mevagissey in the following spring. I suggested
we opened a fishing tackle shop on the other side of the harbour to
the existing one. Bill told me to get on with it, and said he would see
me early in the following year!

Luck was on my side when I was able to rent the shop I had my
eye on. It was situated at the very Western end of the inner harbour,
the opposite side to the other shop. It had a good frontal position and
was also well placed near the lighthouse quay which was frequented by
anglers during the summer and early autumn.

I had been a very keen angler myself until I had taken up fishing for
a living, so I had no difficulty in ordering the stock needed for the
shop. The only problem? Was I over-ordering?

Jack and Babs bought a guest house in the centre of the village, so
it was arranged that Jack should run the shop for us, concentrating on
booking anglers and sharkers. We had several boats prepared to run
angling trips for us as well as good old Eddie Lakeman, a grand character,
who said he would take any surplus sharkers I had over, regardless of
whether there was a full load or not, in the hope that business would
increase for him as we became better known.

I had the shop stocked and ready to open by the time Tim arrived
after Easter. We had a series of long discussions with Mr and Mrs
Wright over advertising, booking systems, rotas, future stock etc.,
after which a company was formed, calling ourselves The Mevagissey
Shark and Angling Centre Ltd.

Shop Does Well

The stock in the shop started to dwindle rapidly after we had been
open a few weeks. Sales increased daily—and I had been worrying
about over-ordering! We had some difficulty obtaining supplies of
tackle from one or two firms, who preferred to supply the already
established shop, but they soon weakened when they found out the
quantity we were selling! I ran anglers until June when sharking
started again.

We had only been running a couple of weeks when Eddie Lakeman mentioned to me that a fine Looe quatter called the *Valhalla* was up for sale, as the owner was retiring. I nipped up to Looe with Tim to have a look at her. We found a typical Looe quatter of thirty-eight feet in length, with a spacious canopy and two very good engines. The overall condition of the boat and gear was excellent.

Returning to Mevagissey I recommended that we should purchase her, which was done a fortnight later. The Valhalla certainly enhanced the sharking business. Bookings increased so much that Eddie's brother Dick was out most days in *Our John* running surplus sharkers that Eddie could not cope with! Bonney and I were very glad of the extra money coming in, for as well as our daughter Carol, we had a fine young baby boy Andrew Richard coming along fast.

I made a lot of good friends while I was running that sharking boat and I'm pleased to say many still call on us when they visit Cornwall to talk over old times and compare children!

The biggest problem sharking skippers have is the weather. Here at Mevagissey every consideration was, and is, given to the customers—after all, they pay to go out. The problem arises when the skipper knows the weather is too bad to take people out to enjoy a days shark fishing properly, yet when told, they either try to insist on going out, or cancel their booking altogether, to go away thoroughly disgruntled.

I have previously mentioned how well sheltered Mevagissey is from the North, West and South. What to the average person is a flat calm day, could be bad weather twelve miles off the land, and to keep in shallow, running away over for Falmouth, would certainly result in better weather in most cases, but a sharkless day. To take the party out having told them the weather was too bad usually resulted in them all flaking out, or asking to come in again half way through the day, and still going away dissatisfied, as we would not refund money once committed to going.

I could tell many yarns about sharking, of the people who do it for the sport, and those who do it for a living. To be a successful sharking skipper you require the patience and tact of a saint, combined with a good knowledge of the sea, and human nature too. I won't elaborate though; the fact that I gave up shark fishing because I found it monotonous doesn't mean that its not a splendid day out to be enjoyed to the full by the holiday maker, and also a very reasonable day out, money-wise.

I'd like to sum up what the boatman is up against in the summer with the following true story. I had four sharkers sitting around, trying to shelter from the driving rain and a strong south west wind. It was around midday, and after some difficulty I had made them all either a cup of tea or coffee. One man, however, refused, saying "I never drink beverages after breakfast, it will spoil my lunch. What time are we leaving for lunch anyway?" I though he was pulling my leg and muttered "You'll be lucky". But to my dismay found he was deadly serious. I never saw him again!

Chapter 9

Trawling

Having tried most methods of fishing, I was keen to have a go at
trawling now we had the *Valhalla*. At one time she had a double
barrelled winch fitted in her. Unfortunately this had been taken out
and sold several years before she changed hands. I shopped around
and finally decided on a hydraulic capstan of one ton pull at a hauling
speed of one hundred feet a minute. To put a mechanical capstan in
meant running a drive and shaft back through the boat with numerous
complications, so for ease of installation the hydraulic one was favourite.

I had no idea what sort of gear to rig up with. There was only one
inshore trawler working from Mevagissey, therefore I was rather
reticent about going along to the owners to ask their advice. Trawl
ground is very limited in our area, so I thought I would be diplomatic
and get on with it as best I could.

I was able to purchase polythene warps, trawl boards, slack back
wires, floats, also a handy otter trawl from a store at Newlyn, where
the manager was extremely helpful. I rigged the trawl up onto a home
made footrope of chain rope and old car tyres cut in strips, which
appeared to be favoured by our local trawler skipper; then with everything measured and connected up, I awaited the arrival of the capstan.

Looking back on it, I think they must have still been inventing it
when we gave them the order, for we got the pump and pipes after
two months and then had to wait a further six weeks for the capstan
head itself.

At last it arrived, being brought down by the sales manager of the
firm. We fixed it on, then found we could not connect it up as we had
to have special heavy duty copper pipe each side of the control tap.

A mate of mine, Bernie Thomas, who had also come from around
the London area originally, was helping me put the capstan in prior
to coming trawling with me. He went up to London that Christmas
to see his parents and triumphantly returned with the right sort of
pipe. Bernie did a good job. His "plumbing" never gave a moment's
trouble when completed, although it was under heavy internal pressure
when the capstan was operating.

We had tried hauling our gear by hand—and quickly decided it

45

was definitely not to be recommended. Local people could always tell when we had been out for our arms were so stretched, our fingers nearly dragged on the ground when we walked! I often felt like crawling home, I was that snookered after a happy day's shetting and hauling our onion bag, as I called it.

But once we got the capstan going, life was definitely made a lot easier for us. I proceeded to catch every rock, stone, oil drum, tractor tyre, tin can, bush or bottle that resided either temporarily or permanently around Mevagissey. We went further afield, both East and West. To the westward we found plenty of hitches combined with lavish bags of seaweed. To the east'ard we specialised in huge muddy bags of sea urchins, star fish and old sea shells, varied with milk crates, orange cases, barbed wire, old crab pots and if we were very lucky, as a special treat, we would get a whole blackthorn bush, or perhaps the trunk and top branches of an old apple tree pinned into the trawl from top to bottom!

We did catch some fish as well. By plugging away steadily, I found the clear ground; also, we made a few alterations to our gear which in turn improved the catches. By the end of the spring we were doing quite well, while I had become so interested in the job and the many problems it presented, that I was loath to start the sharking season again, in spite of the fact it was much easier work physically.

Bernie took over a sharking and angling boat for the Shark Centre in May, so I had to stow away the gear prior to painting up for the forthcoming shark season. People came in droves that year. To me it became like bus driving, one load after another. The weather was excellent, so we just went on and on and on. There were plenty of sharks. I even started to feel sorry for them as I gaffed them, clobbered them, washed them, then laid them out in neat rows to be shown off and photographed by the proud captors and admiring crowds at the end of the trip. Still, it was a record season for business and that's what we did it for.

The boat Bernie had been running for the Shark Centre that season was called the *Topaz*, a very fast quatter type vessel with a Perkins SM6 diesel. Bernie wished to buy it from us, so rather than retain him against his will, we sold him the boat and I asked Albert if he would come along for the winter season with me. Albert was pleased to come along; although he had not done any trawling previously, he soon settled in, becoming as keen as I was.

I find Trawls are Tricky Things

On finding that our flat fish trawl had its limitations, we ordered a Boris box trawl. When it arrived it seemed a simple matter to put it aboard and then go fishing. No such luck!

We tried it, altered floats, altered the weight of the footrope, also trying various combinations of chain, wires and slackbacks.

Slowly it dawned on us that all we hadn't tried was larger boards, which we were lucky enough to buy secondhand locally.

After further trial and error, we got things to our satisfaction and were well rewarded with both white and flat fish.

Two days catches during that period will always stick in my memory though. We were towing along about three miles from Polperro, when our warps came together, at the same time we almost stopped. Knocking out, we hauled immediately thinking we had a large stone in the trawl.

It took us about an hour to lift our "stone" up the 30 fathoms until it hung from the stern just under the surface. The belly of the net was ripped out back to the cod end, so Albert leant right over the rail gathering up the slack net before he put another strop around it prior to us hauling it right aboard.

He suddenly straightened up with his eyes open so wide that his prominent eyebrows had disappeared completely beneath his woollen hat.

"My Chwist, boy, there's a bloody geet bomb, my Chwist ther is!" he spluttered, running for'ard to where I stood by the capstan, probably with my mouth wide open.

Taking a turn round the back with the rope I'd been taking off, I went aft to see what it was Albert had mistaken for a bomb. Looking down through the rip in the net, I felt all the hair on the back of my neck stand up. Albert had not been mistaken! At the top was a large circle of metal, from the centre of which extended four fins welded to the outside. A large grey egg shaped cylinder reposed beneath!

Being a cowardly soul, I smartly started to cut the net. Two touches of the knife were enough for the net with its catch to snap, run, then go plummetting down, while Albert went ahead hard on both engines in case it went off when it hit the bottom, which fortunately it didn't.

We had drifted over some rough ground by the time I had cut the cod end away, so there was no chance of it being trawled up again by anyone else. We later found that it had been an anti-submarine missile, shot from a destroyer during a practice just after the last war. Of the dozen fired, six have now been recovered. They had failed to explode because they were released in thirty fathoms but set to go off at forty!

The second catch was not so hair raising and was far more profitable. During that winter there had been a break in the Southerly gale that had been blowing for almost a week. Albert and I had got the Boris box trawl working well by then, but we had not encountered any quantity of whiting. So on the first morning the wind eased, we shot off up to the Polperro grounds, in the hopes of a day's work in the very thick water.

It was a fisherman's dream come true. Our wet paper fish finder showed us heavy concentrations of fish from top to bottom. We shot and towed through the thickest of them for an hour and a half, by which time we had slowed right up. On hauling we found about four baskets of whiting, a basket of cod and pollack and also a good basket of flats, mostly brill and turbot.

We shot away for another hour and a half. This time we had twice as much fish and had to double bag it, to get it aboard!

The third tow lasted only an hour. We were so busy gutting, I allowed the boat to wander too near the rough bottom, consequently we came fast, perhaps just as well, as by this time the wind had freshened to give us a good dusting on our homeward run.

The strong winds lasted a further fortnight. When we returned to the grounds things were back to normal, but it had been a day to remember. Four hours actual towing had resulted in one hundred and four stone of whiting, sixteen stone of cod and pollock, sixteen stone of prime flats. Normally a couple of baskets of mixed for two hours was received thankfully.

In the spring of the following year we lost the box trawl in the wreck of the *Twilight Waters*, a Plymouth trawler that had been blown to smithereens with the loss of all hands after she had hauled a mine in her trawl whilst fishing off Falmouth just after the last war. We made do with the smaller trawl for a few weeks, then started to paint and varnish up for the sharking season again. But this time we had decided to try to purchase a larger trawler, leaving Albert to run the *Valhalla* during the summer; then he would join me again for trawling in the winter. I had met a chap from Par earlier that year who had agreed to come with me if we could get a suitable boat.

Sharking started as usual at the end of May. Albert joined me to learn the ropes while we answered advertisement after advertisement in *Fishing News* in our endeavours to get a boat suitable for our particular needs.

Chapter 10

Forming a co-op: Mevagissey Fisheries Ltd.

MEVAGISSEY fishermen always had several fish merchants to whom they could dispose of their catches. You chose your buyer, then landed to him.

When I started fishing I made enquiries as to who was the best buyer of the existing three to deal with, and was told by all and sundry there was not a ha'porth of difference to choose between them. To my surprise I found that the largest concern fixed the price which the other two followed. Fish was taken, cleaned, iced, then sent off to the various inland markets. When it had been sold at that market, and only then, would the fishermen know what they would be paid. The buyers never bought a fish until it had been sold!

To ensure a good return to the merchant, with no risk attached, fish at the end of the week was always a lot cheaper than earlier on, although in many cases it was held over the weekend to make a very substantial extra profit on the following Monday's markets.

The fishermen at Mevagissey had to work hard just to survive under the system of fish marketing that existed there. The buyers had it all their own way. In fairness to them, it had gone on so long that it had become an accepted way of life, with the buyer never looking to the future and the fishermen generally becoming too old to see any way of altering things, or even wishing to.

Very few young men took up fishing after I came to Mevagissey. Every year saw boats being sold out of the town, going away mostly to be converted to pleasure craft, while the crews either retired or bought smaller boats in which they catered for the holiday trade, and did a bit of inshore fishing in the off seasons. Boats like the *Manxman, Hopeful, Margaret, Pride of the West, Spray, Red Ace, White Heather, Endeavour, Sea Gull, Bonny Girls, Liberty, Britannia, Ibis,* all went, never to be replaced. So it came about that coupled with the failure of the winter pilchard seasons and also the lack of

49

long line fish during the summer months, one, then another, of the
fish merchants closed down. This left one merchant with all the fishermen on his hands; that is, if he could cope with them, and on what terms.

I saw that the time was right to form a Fishermen's Co-operative,
but as I had already tried to do this ten years before, and had been
met with such apathy that I quickly gave up in disgust, I decided to
watch points this time and let the others start the ball rolling.

The first general meeting of fishermen was a negative free for all;
the second, soon after, was a much better affair, although it was still
poorly attended. Mr Alec Sharples, the White Fish Authority's area
officer from Plymouth attended, and the late W. D. Mogridge who
was the secretary and manager of the newly formed Brixham Fisher-
mans' Co-operative.

I had heard rumours that some fishermen had hopes of buying one
of the large premises on the quay which had belonged to one of the
now retired fish buyers. I knew this would be impossible, as no loans
or grants were available for secondhand properties under the White
Fish Authority's Development Schemes. As soon as the meeting
opened, Mr Sharples explained the impossibility of purchasing the
premises. A bit of a ding dong followed and there was much dis-
appointment shown; so after Mr Mogridge had given us a pep talk,
which was followed by Mr Sharples who pledged his and the Authority's
support if we could get organized amongst ourselves, I outlined a
plan I had conceived to pack and send our fish to Newlyn and Plymouth
markets.

I was elected to head an action committee to look into it further, and
a few weeks later the Co-operative was formed. I had the honour of
being elected Chairman, a retired gentleman Mr Pardoe, volunteered
to be the Society's secretary, and this offer was gratefully accepted.
The Committee were all fishermen, a very undiplomatic but determined
bunch of characters. We had only a few weeks to get running. There
were no premises, refrigeration or transport! Some fishermen joined
us because they believed we could succeed, others joined in desperation, while quite a few decided to play safe by carrying on fishing for
the remaining buyer.

I must confess I was worried when we opened for subscriptions on
a Saturday morning, but I need not have been. A steady stream of
stalwarts turned up, some with cheques, some with bundles of notes
so old they were verging on antique value! By 2 p.m. that day we had
raised £2,500 and by the end of the week a further £700. Mevagissey
Fisheries Ltd. was really happening.

We were extremely fortunate to get the services of Jimmy Furze,
who volunteered to work for us as Manager, storeman, driver, clerk,
packer and general factotum!

Our next job was to get transport. With money to burn we rushed off to Truro and spent a whole £50 on an old Morris Laundry van! What a van it was! Loaded well above its capacity, it travelled to Newlyn sometimes twice a day loaded with mackerel and later with other types of fish, and then returned with sacks of ice for the next load.

We ordered a new and much larger lorry soon after, as it was obvious we would never cope when landings increased with the approach of better weather. We managed to buy boxes, baskets, scales, kits, a crane with many other bits and pieces from one of the retired merchants.

During this time furious negotiations were going on for the erection of premises with refrigeration facilities on the West Wharf. Everyone was very helpful. We drew up a plan of what we needed, then the following year, after piles of red tape had been waded through, we eventually got our building which we rented from the Harbour Authorities, who built it with the aid of a grant. We had a small store attached to a 1500 cubic foot cold room, and the quay was roofed in from there to its eastern end.

We have to thank the Ministry of Agriculture and Fisheries, the White Fish Authority, the Mevagissey Harbour Trustees and above all Mr A. Sharples and Mr W. H. Williams District Inspector of Fisheries, Plymouth for their unrelenting efforts to get us fixed up. I also had a great deal of correspondence with Mr W. J. Lord the former Secretary of the Fisheries Organisation Society Ltd. whose information and advice on the best procedure to be followed in setting up our own organization was highly valuable.

It's Not an Easy Job

We had our moments though! Don't ever believe forming and running a fishermens co-operative is easy. Alf Pardoe resigned after twelve months, as he intended going to New Zealand to live. I don't think we drove him there, I hope not anyway, for he looked all right when he came back to visit us recently!

His place was filled by a fisherman, Passmore Williams. I was still chairman, also now having a vice-chairman, Colin Williams, while the Committee stayed about the same. Passmore did a wonderful job. Colin Williams was a schoolmaster who fished part-time. That's how he put it! I've never known quite how he stands, as he's a damned good teacher, but a better fisherman than most as well. Anyway, he shakes us up sometimes when we need it, sometimes when we don't!

The Committee had by this time got used to working together and all in all we weren't a bad little set-up. The reader must excuse me if I appear a little smug at this point of my narrative. What we achieved we did together, and I'm pleased I was able to do my share towards its formation.

Looking back on our progress over the last four years, I can view it with pleasure, and some considerable frustration. We made a few hundred pounds profit the first year, more each successive year. The remaining merchant closed down his wholesale and retail business which enabled us to open a wet fish shop of our own on the quay. We have a very hard working lorry driver on the staff, and a thriving wholesale trade with local fishmongers, but like most small businesses we are being throttled by taxation. If we keep any legitimate profit back in reserve, nearly half of it has to be paid out as Corporation Tax.

Taxation and Bureaucracy

Think of it! A group of fishermen form a Co-operative to enable them to carry on in their chosen calling. Assistance is given initially by various government departments to get them going. As soon as they start really getting organised, in come the forms, the letters, the directives. This snowballs to such a pitch that a lady has to come in to deal with it every morning of the week and most of it is "bumff" believe me!

A large proportion of the Co-op's income stems directly from carriage deducted from the catches on a poundage basis. When there is a surplus at the end of the year, we have to pay it all back regardless of our future needs, otherwise "pop goes the weasel" or something like that. I know we can earmark set sums of money for specific needs, but in our industry how do we know from one week to the next what our requirements, incoming or outgoing, will be? It is time for someone in authority to take a long hard look at taxation laws where they apply to small co-operatives like ours at Mevagissey, also at the amount of "bumff" showered at will all over the country on the long suffering populace. We run a business at Mevagissey with a turnover of around £100,000 per annum. There are three full-time men and a part-time woman with a committee of volunteers. How would Whitehall cope with that I wonder? Parkinson had the right idea!

We have got through this last year quite well, in spite of a serious strike of fish workers at Newlyn. This unfortunate affair has now been settled, but has meant a considerable fall in income for us here during the winter—Newlyn fish merchants had to almost come to a standstill in their trading, and as all our mackerel went there, we had to stop fishing for most of the duration of the strike. It is obvious that we, as a Co-operative, will have to diversify our distributive activities in the future, so that should labour troubles again hold up fish distribution anywhere we can send elsewhere, and maintain the Co-op's and the community's income, which is essential for our economic survival as a group relying on fishing for a living.

The Fisheries Organisation Society Ltd., which was first registered

in 1914 under the Industrial and Provident Societies Act of 1893
has given our Co-operative most welcome advice and assistance
during and since our formation. The Society was formed along the
lines of the already existing Agricultural Organization Society in the
United Kingdom and its objects are broadly as follows:

1. The formation and development of fishermens' co-operative
   societies at the inshore fishing stations in England and Wales with
   a view to the improved organisation of the collection, sale and
   distribution of fish and fishing products;
2. Co-operative hire or purchase of fishing requisites;
3. The Co-operative working of shell fish beds;
4. The promotion of the consumption of fish generally;
5. The prevention of encroachment on the rights of fishing;
6. The collection and circulation of information as to fresh markets;
   new methods, etc.;
7. Close liaison with the Ministry of Agriculture, Fisheries and
   Food, the White Fish Authority, the Sea Fisheries Committees
   and other bodies, on matters affecting the welfare of the inshore
   fishermen of England and Wales;
8. The insurance of inshore fishing vessels (carried out by an allied
   Society, the Fishing Vessels Co-operative Insurance Society Ltd.).

   The Society offers advisory assistance to inshore fishermen and also
to Governmental departments connected with the industry in matters
relating to subsidy arrangements, fishing limits negotiations, etc. etc.
Mevagissey Fisheries Ltd. Co-operative is affiliated to the F.O.S.
and further information about this most excellent Society can be
obtained from the Secretary, Fisheries Organization Society Ltd.,
Denison House, 296 Vauxhall Bridge Road, Westminster, London
SW1V 1AE (Telephone 01 834 5657).

Chapter 11

We buy the 'Ros Guill'

JUST when it looked as though I was destined to spend another season sharking, we had a reply from Swansea in South Wales, enclosing details of a fifty-foot seine netter converted to trawling. It looked all right on paper, so I contacted Dave Hooper and off we went to look her over.

The weather was very hot I remember. We got accommodation right on the front, and I was glad of the breeze which blew in from the sea as it cooled me off during the night. We weren't far from the fish docks, so it was only a few minutes walk from our digs to where we met the owner for our inspection the following morning.

We could not fault the boat, except that she stood a lot higher out of the water than I would have liked. Being a seiner she had a very high deck and very low rails. The engine was an 88 Kelvin diesel situated for'ard. On the deck over the engine was a four speed seine trawl winch. The boat was fitted with wireless, two banks of good batteries and Decca Navigator.

To those who have never heard of a Decca Navigator, it is best described as simply as possible as an indispensable item of equipment for anyone contemplating working a trawler full time away from land. It consists of a wireless receiver which is built to activate four clocks on its face. Each of the three clocks receives a different signal from the others, whilst another clock is made to receive all three lanes or channels, and is the master one of the four. Decca Charts are divided into Red, Green and Purple lines radiating from slave and master wireless stations ashore. It is a simple matter to learn your exact position day and night, with no margin of error possible provided the operator checks and cross checks his bearings properly. It is also possible to tow in any given area and avoid wrecks, snags etc. whose positions are known, as you go along. The usual method is to tow along straight lines, which are lettered and numbered for the operator's convenience.

There were a pair of wooden trawl boards, reinforced in the usual way with iron, also a pair of steel V form doors. We also found a couple of trawls, one new, while the other was all ropes and rumpy!

We returned to Mevagissey to report on our findings, and went back a couple of weeks later. This time we were to fit the boat out and bring her back to Mevagissey.

We took several boxes and bundles of gear with us on the train, and were glad to be met when we arrived at Swansea station by a chap with a pick-up who drove us down to the boat with all our bits and pieces. He had even had the stove in the cabin going for a few days to air it out properly for us. This we greatly appreciated, so that we were left with nothing to do but to get some provisions in before the shops closed that afternoon. Hoopie, as I nicknamed David, was a good cook, so we had an excellent evening meal before turning in early to be ready for a good start the next morning.

We spent a week getting organised, and finding our way around. Painting, cleaning, minor repairs, checking electrics, the engine, mending the trawls, also in purchasing and marking some trawl warps which we badly needed, as the originals were too far gone for safety.

We made several friends, and got a lot of information and help from other fishermen using the dock. Having the Decca fitted, I was able to mark out a lot of tows in the Camarthen Bay area which were willingly given to us by two of the local skippers, whose boats were also equipped with Decca. Hoopie had been mate on a coaster for a year or two before coming with me, so was fully conversant with the "box of tricks". It was a good job for both of us he was, as it took me a couple of days at sea to really become familiar with those four little clocks!

We had decided to have a trip or two from Swansea before coming home, but as soon as we were ready the weather turned poor and blew hard from the South-west. This gave us time to learn about Swansea

Swansea is a curious mixture of the old and the new. The centre of the town, demolished by heavy bombing during the last war, was rebuilt with wide streets, modern buildings and a general air of spaciousness while the area around the fish docks remained old, dirty and very depressing. In spite of this, the people living there were extremely friendly and cheerful, so although weather bound we had an enjoyable time, working on the boat and gear during the days, then spending our evenings having a drink or going into the centre of the town for a meal. We had a steady stream of locals calling on us when we were aboard, our char or coffee mornings were very popular. We talked shop of course, as fishermen do in all parts of the world, but I was learning all the time, much appreciating the advice offered, glad to hear of and discuss different methods of working as applied to the immediate areas around the Welsh coast.

Lucky First Trawl

We put a ton of flake ice aboard as soon as the weather looked like improving, then three days later set off for Camarthen Bay. Our original intention had been to fish the grounds South and South West of Swansea as soles were abundant there at that time of the year, but with freshening Westerlies forecast we decided to play it safe.

We shot as soon as we passed the Worms Head, then towed in straight for the Western corner of the bay and were glad of the shelter as we got into the lee of the land. After two hours we hauled, mainly to check if all gear was working properly. We saw there was plenty of fish in the bag and on releasing the cod-end were delighted to find about forty stone of thornback ray, forty stone of mostly small and intermediate plaice, with a few soles for extra measure.

Down went the gear again for a four hour drag. The wind continued to freshen, so we kept well inside the bay, hauling again just before dusk. What a bag came up. Quite apart from over a hundred stone of flats our trawl was a solid mass of enormous jelly fish!

We shot again, then started to clean up the foredeck and starboard waterway. Only about thirty stone of the flats were sizeable—we picked out what we could, then opened the waterway slides to send the rest cascading away in a long white trail astern. We tried towing off again, but the sea had made up alarmingly in the extremely shallow water, so we reluctantly turned back. We spent the next two days and nights inside the bay hauling in enormous bags of flats, most of which had to be shovelled overboard again as being too small. Dawn on the third morning saw us so tired we didn't know whether it was Christmas or Easter, so I decided to run to Swansea. Running was the operative word. With a force seven Westerly under our tail it was more like surf boarding, but the boat rose to the occasion better than we had hoped for, and gave us a relatively smooth run back to the docks.

Arriving around midday we crawled into our bunks. Neither of us knew any more until one of the fish workers called us the following morning at five. We had several willing helpers to assist us unloading. Hoopie had rigged up the derrick, I shovelled out, while he swung the baskets ashore. Even then I shovelled fish out of her for nearly two hours. It turned out to be a well paid trip. We had the quantity, if not the quality, but I've never worked so hard before or since. I can still see the boat covered in fish, us trying to sort it, then turning away over three quarters of it again.

On the next trip we caught less, but made more money as the weather enabled us to fish out further. Our catch yielded more ray and soles without the large quantities of immature fish.

There was no sign of the weather settling though, so we decided to leave for home as soon as we had a fine day or two. Our 88 Kelvin was apparently in first class condition and was running well, but I did not want to risk breaking down off the north coast of Cornwall or Devon with strong westerly winds. We landed a further trip on the Thursday then waited until the following Sunday before setting sail.

It was a beautiful day, only a light breeze from the Nor'West disturbed the water. All went well. We reached Land's End just as the sun was beginning to set in a blaze of red and orange light to the West'ard. The sea was now undisturbed by any wind, the oily swell reflected the sunset and sky in beautiful flashes of colour while the cliffs glowed warm and tall as we motored on between the land and the Longships lighthouse, which stands sentinel on the treacherous black reefs like a monument to all those poor souls who were drowned there before the rocks were properly marked.

We weren't long getting around to Newlyn on the flood tide, where we spent the night. The following morning we purchased floats, ropes, shackles, twines, with other odds and ends needed to fit us up properly, and then sailed for Mevagissey with a fine breeze of South Easterly wind. We arrived at tea time to a great welcome from Carol and Andrew, who must have thought I had been away far too long judging from the noise they made as they raced round the harbour to where we tied up for the night.

Chapter 12

Queer catches and curry

Hoopie and I worked locally for several weeks and found the Decca invaluable for trawling on patchy ground. We discovered new ground over South sou'west of Mevagissey, which although extremely dirty, through being covered with sea urchins, dead shells and worm cases, had plenty of fish on it.

We made up two new trawls, then the first night we shot, one of them caught an aeroplane engine in it. We got it up alongside, but before we could strap it up, it rolled down from the mouth of the trawl and took most of the net with it! The rest of the night went well, plenty of lemon soles, megrims also several stones of large dover soles, but the "piece de resistance" was to come on the next trip.

A friend of mine, Rodney Ingram, was home on leave from his job as wireless officer on a large freighter, so he asked if he could come out with us the following evening. It was a windless night with hardly any swell. Owing to the nature of the bottom we were towing for only one hour at a time, catching plenty of fish and a lot of rubbish each drag. I had marked the exact spot on the chart where our aeroplane engine had dropped away the night before, and as we had worked the patch of ground several times without mishap we thought we were in for a clear time to come. The second drag of the evening resulted in an enormous bag of rubbish which was swung inboard without mishap. On freeing the cod end knot, there was a resounding clump on the deck followed by a cascade of shells, urchins and fish.

When we had hauled the trawl that time, there had been several lengths of shiny wire connected to a couple of smallish brass-like metal calibrated gauges. We thought they were further pieces off the aeroplane and threw them down for'side of the wheelhouse to look at in our leisure.

I realised then that whatever had thudded onto the deck under the mound of muck was probably either a large stone or something that had been connected to the pieces we had taken out of the wings. So I took a shovel and carefully cleared the top layer of rubbish from around "the thing". I spotted a piece of wire, so put down the shovel, and cleared the rest of the stuff away by hand.

Another wire came to light, leading down to a yellowed metal cylinder about the size of a half pint bottle; one wire went into each side of this through small projecting knobs. I had already realised we were in possession of something probably dangerous, and on clearing away the debris around it we found we had a large black metal cylinder, slightly domed at the top with the wires and attachments screwed into its centre. The side of the cylinder shone like a new shilling where the wire and chain had scuffed it as we had towed over it, so the container was obviously in perfect condition.

I called up Falmouth Coastguards on the radio telephone immediately, telling them we had a dangerous looking object aboard and that it was too heavy to manhandle over the side without jarring or knocking it.

They advised us to anchor well out in the bay and await the arrival of the Royal Navy Mine Disposal squad, which they had notified at Plymouth.

We cruised in slowly to avoid undue deck vibration, then anchored as instructed. A good friend of mine, Robin Vinnicombe gamely turned out of his bed to come out in his boat the *Internoss* to take us ashore, where we waited until the Disposal Squad arrived, and then he ran us out again. He even offered to give us a hand with "the thing" but we thanked him profusely, suggesting he should return to bed and leave it to the experts!

An hour after the Disposal Squad had come aboard not one of us was any the wiser! The thing sat on the deck, we all sat down in the cabin drinking coffee, thumbing through manual after manual of mines, bombs, torpedoes and other diabolical devices, all guaranteed to ease man from this earth with big bangs and generally, sudden deaths.

A further half hour went by, when a trainee attached to the four man team blurted out "I've got it!"

One of the other chaps turned to look.

"You've got the bloody book upside down you great steaming nit!"

He was right. The Lieutenant in charge of the party congratulated the lad, then explained to us what it was.

There was much excitement from the lads when they found out just what we had caught, as it was the first one they had ever come across. It was the charge case, detonator, firing mechanisms and wiring complete, less the whole of the mine casing which had been eaten away with age. It was a German mine sown at the outbreak of the 1914-18 war, and the case contained 350 pounds of T.N.T. As they said, we wouldn't have needed the squad if it had fallen out of the trawl the other way up!

We hoisted it off, and dropped it in fairly shallow water in the middle of the bay. We also buoyed it, so they could explode it at daylight.

We went in for a few hours sleep. The disposal boys called back on us to say that it had gone off with a lovely wallop, and asked if they could have the pieces for their museum, which we gladly gave them!

Soon after this episode we decided to shift up to Plymouth for the autumn, shipping on Albert as third hand for the winter.

Too Much Curry

Albert and Dave were never really kindly disposed towards each other when aboard boat. I suppose the main cause of discontent was Dave's love of curry—which I ate sparingly and Albert detested. Even the smell would infuriate Albert, who would walk round muttering dark threats on how he would one day boil Hoopie alive in a bath of his own bloody curry!

Dave had purchased what seemed to be a never ending supply of curry powder from a chandler at Swansea. It was in a large round tin which he kept carefully hidden as soon as Albert joined us. The end of that tin came dramatically on a Saturday night, and had Dave been smaller, or Albert bigger, Davie would probably have joined the curry tin in the bottom of Sutton Harbour!

We had been fishing hard, winding up the week on Saturday morning. Albert went off with Dave shopping, and came back with a good supply of meat, vegetables, bread, bacon, eggs etc. for the weekend. We had lived quite a bit out of the frying pan that week so the thought of a nice stew with a good supply of Davie's speciality dumplings floating around in it was a vision which Albert looked forward to throughout the rest of that day.

We had a snack lunch, a drink in the "Dolphin", then after putting the large iron pot of stew on to simmer, we turned in for a well earned afternoon nap. We turned out, washed, changed, then Albert hopped ashore for some cigarettes. I went on deck with a mug of tea, leaving Davie to tidy up prior to dishing up the stew.

Albert returned, and remarking he was starving, shot down the ladder to the cabin, to take his place expectantly at the table, closely followed by me. Davie put three great plates of stew on the table, and immediately my heart sank. The stench of curry filled the cabin. Albert was so obsessed with getting his plateful inside of him that he had taken two mouthfuls before the awful truth dawned on him. Banging his spoon down onto the table he let forth such a stream of abuse at Davie I wondered if he would ever stop. It flowed out of him like poetry. Fortunately he couldn't get at Davie as I was wedging him in, and I had no intention of the evening starting with a brawl.

Slowly Albert's protestations subsided, I managed half my stew, having to concede to the curry powder when my ears nearly dropped off with the burning in my throat.

Albert ate bread and jam glaring blackly at Davie who had eaten his own plateful and had started on Albert's.

"Come on Albert, we'll go up the 'Dolphin' for a pint, Davie can join us there" I tactfully suggested.

"Right, boy, then I can get some fish and chips on the way up to the pictures" he replied.

We had a few in the "Dolphin", being joined by Davie who was so bloated with his blasted curry he could only drink a couple of small bottles.

Suddenly Dave started nattering that it was time to get up the road or we'd miss the film. Albert loved the pictures, so decided to forgo his fish and chips until we came out. Several times during the show he said to me how he was looking forward to his visit to the chip shop, and as soon as we came out he was off down the road like an electric hare.

Before we reached the shop I guessed what had happened; a fire engine was parked outside surrounded by a fair sized crowd of on-lookers. Albert's fish and chips had gone up in smoke when the fryer had caught fire!

Albert went back aboard to some more bread and jam, muttering horribly. Wherever Davie had kept the curry powder hidden, Albert found it, as Davie never did again.

We never had curry again while Albert was aboard with us, although we did have a little bit sneaked in stews at a later date but in eatable quantities!

Another "Peculiar" Fish

Fishing from Plymouth was good that Autumn. We decided to move to Newlyn in the New Year so we left Albert at Mevagissey to get the *Valhalla* ready, and shipped on Rodney Ingram's brother Stewart. I could write a book about Stewart, mostly unprintable, but surprisingly we are still very good friends.

While fishing down there about fourteen miles off we came fast and couldn't break out. We eventually lifted what we were fast in by taking slack wire, passing it over a fairlead on the quarter, then hauling it on the starboard whipping drum. We decided to try to tow it in.

We came fast at seven in the evening, and arrived back in Newlyn at 2 p.m. the following afternoon! A skin diver came out to clear our gear which we had buoyed in shallow water off Mousehole.

He reported we had towed in two great iron girders from a steamer's hatch surrounds, a piece of a ship's bridge, a huge open steel cylinder twenty feet long over three feet wide and the complete trawl, chains, floats, bobbins etc. lost from a much larger trawler. All this was towed in on one and a half inch wire warp terminating in a half inch galvanised iron shackle which had closed right up and held! *And that really is the truth.*

Of our trawl there remained only the footrope, but we made nearly three nice trawls out of the one we had salvaged, so our persistency was at least rewarded in part. Newlyn was a bad season for us due entirely to the weather which was the worst experienced for years. Strong South Easterly or South Westerly winds persisted, so at the end of February we decided to return to Mevagissey.

Chapter 13

I come ashore—
to more fish

WHILST fishing from Plymouth during the previous September I had to come home with an infection in both legs due to standing at the wheel for long periods without adequate rest.

I had always suffered from varicose veins, but until then had just put up with them. I had got out of my bunk one Saturday morning to find that as soon as I stood on my feet I experienced terrible stabbing pains up my legs and particularly in my groins. I had noticed a few twinges for days prior to this, but realised this time something had really gone wrong.

I sat down on the locker for a while then stood up again. The pain made me sweat profusely, so telling the lads I had better get home quickly, I caught the first train back to St Austell, our nearest station to Mevagissey. The pains had eased during the day, but I called into my doctor's that evening, who diagnosed infected veins, aggravated by too much standing.

The following day I saw a specialist at St Austell hospital who gave me some tablets then put my name down for an exploratory operation and told me to stand up as little as possible! My doctor had given me seven days off, and told me to look in at the end of the week to see how I was progressing. So I pottered about at home, celebrated my birthday during the week and had an enjoyable time with Bonny and the children.

I had visited my parents, finding them both very well. Mother had been poorly prior to this with a nervous breakdown aggravated by a dispute with the neighbours over a right of way around their property. I had done all I could, but it was obvious to me the matter would eventually have to be resolved legally, so it had been left in the hands of the respective solicitors. Two days after my birthday I was sitting watching television about eight in the evening when there was a knock on the door. It was a friend of my parents who lived opposite them.

"I think your father's just died, come up quickly" he blurted out.

I went with him to find Dad dead, sitting in his favourite chair where he had been watching television with Mum. I took Mum home with me, where she stayed until after Christmas. The shock had been too much for her, although we all did what was in our power, especially Bonny, who was wonderful with her. Mum suffered a complete mental breakdown and in the New Year went voluntarily into St Lawrence's Hospital at Bodmin.

Things piled up for me after that. The dispute over the right of way around my parents' house continued, my little boy was due for an operation in Falmouth, while I awaited one also. I was trying to be in several places at once as well as run the boat, that in itself being one person's job, so I suppose what happened was inevitable. Early in March I got out of bed one Monday morning, and found myself unable to stop shaking. To say I felt ill would have been the understatement of the year.

I crept down to the doctor and he took one look at me and told me to have at least a month's holiday. I did not realise what was wrong with me even then, but after a long talk with the doctor I realised I had been overdoing it for the past six months, so, clutching a large bottle of tranquilizer pills I went home to think things out.

After mooning around home for a few days, I reluctantly came to the same conclusion that my doctor had reached in a few seconds, so I went off to tell Mr Wright and Tim that I should have to come ashore; also that under the circumstances I might not return to sea for some time. They took the news far better than I had expected. They probably guessed beforehand the nature of my visit, both being highly intelligent people. With that load off my mind I got cracking on the wilderness that had been our back garden, but after a week or two got the itch and applied for a job as a life insurance salesman, which to my surprise I got.

Lured Back to Fish

Andrew had his operation successfully soon after I started my new job, then poor old Mum died. It was a happy release for all concerned as she had been terribly ill beth mentally and physically. In my new job I spent most of my time driving around Cornwall, also going three times a week to Launceston, which was our nearest office. I shared my transport with Jeff Graydon who lived at Lostwithial, which was *en route*. We would give each other lifts on alternate trips.

Jeff was married and had a little girl. He had been at sea prior to taking the insurance job and was not at all happy with his lot. The amount of motoring involved was also getting me down, so one day when driving home I suggested we should set up as fishmongers. Jeff already knew I was a bit "nutty" so he thought about it for a while, watching me out of the corner of his eye in case I had a further brainstorm.

We discussed the matter further, during the following days, and decided that our best course of action was to get a van, set of scales etc. and just get going.

Our first van was a 15 cwt. Bedford. Jeff covered the floor and sealed it with alloy sheeting. We bought a collection of new and second-hand bins, a portable sink unit, and a few knives, price tickets and a couple of white coats each.

As soon as our scales were delivered we were ready to launch ourselves on the unsuspecting public. I had a short letter typed and duplicated telling people all about ourselves and that we would be calling on a certain day at such a time.

Armed with great yaffles of folded letters, we put one through every letter box we could find on our proposed rounds. When we couldn't find a letter box, which was surprisingly often, we knocked, to get some very queer responses.

Both Jeff and I had been selling life insurance in £1,000, £2,000 or £2,500 units, calling uninvited and unannounced, so a few minutes spent getting a person to take one of our letters was just keeping our hands in as it were!

Some ladies would rush out of their front doors to collect, thinking we were delivering soap coupons or some other free offer; others would peer around their front room curtains and then, when we knocked, would pretend they were out.

The amount of stuff pushed through letter boxes generally must make some people very wary indeed, as on many occasions a top bedroom window would be thrown open, followed by a worried face shouting, "Not today thank you!"

The best way to deal with these we found was either to reply, "It certainly won't be until next week, dear, that is if we've got any left by the time we reach here" or "Don't worry dear, if you do want any next week ask your neighbours to get it!"

Once you could get them talking, this type of person often turned out to be a very good customer.

We bought most of our fish from the Co-operative at Mevagissey. We kept our bins and fish in the cold room there at night, sharing a corner of it with Billy Moore, a grand character who had been in the trade all his life, but who had only started up on his own a year or so before us.

New Skills Required

I knew what fish was, but to be a fishmonger is a completely different department to catching it, and Bill Moore helped me tremendously with his advice in the first few months of our new venture. I had to learn to fillet plaice, whiting, pollock, cod, mackerel, skin soles and ray, and above all how to prepare fish without wastage, which sometimes meant the difference between profit and loss.

I spent many evenings that autumn filleting fish down the Co-op quay with Bill doing the same, I did not have to go any further for my entertainment for I often got a better show watching and listening to Bill than people did seeing a variety spectacular on the television.

One of Bill's famous sayings could no doubt be used to good effect in the cut-throat world of everyday advertising. Slicing off the side of a particularly well-conditioned fish he would cradle it in his hands then say with mock sincerity laced with emotion: "You know—fish like this—it's much too good for the working man!" I used to almost believe him myself!

Jeff and I often chuckle when we look back on our first few months together. Filleting a plaice was a major operation, I usually nicked myself sometime during the day with the filleting knife, and in the cold weather my hands were often so numb it was a while before I noticed.

One freezing cold day a very refined lady came out to our van; after she had sized up our display and prices very carefully she surprised me by asking for a large fillet of cod, which was not very brilliant for quality on that particular day. To my horror when I picked it up to weigh it, I saw it had a great splodge of blood on it, glancing at my hand, I saw I'd done it again! Quick thinking was needed, so transferring the fillet back to the tray with my right hand I dexterously wiped the blood from my other hand onto my overall on her blind side, at the same time muttering something about the other fillets looked thicker.

"Oh no don't put that one back" she said "I know really fresh fish when I see it, I want that piece there with the blood running out of it". She got it!

We bought a second van just before Christmas that year. It had been a gown van, coach built, very roomy inside with plenty of headroom. Jeff did the floor with alloy sheeting then we put a non-slip rubber mat up through the centre. There were two steps up then trays of fish each side with the scales, cutting block and more fish up at the front which extended over the cab. Done out in high gloss white paint the whole effect was very pleasing, the two big advantages being shelter for the customer and very easy work for myself. Most of my stock was kept iced in a stack of aluminium bins easily accessible as they were kept under the counters. The bottom bin of each stack collected the drainings. Because it was so sheltered for the customers, it proved to have its disadvantages too. The fish man coming around brought together people who only saw each other perhaps once a week. So on a cold, wet and windy day the van would be packed with old dears discussing their latest operations or "that girl down the road". Sometimes they got quite carried away with their gossip, and gave little regard to me who wanted to serve them and get off down the road to my next call.

Jeff was always a tearaway at the best of times, standing no nonsense from anyone, and hurtling from call to call like a jet propelled fish-filled missile! If it was cold and wet, those customers who didn't brave the elements that day when he called, usually saw him fly past the following week only stopping at someone's house who was a bit keener. I heard many tales of quite robust women sprinting up the road like four minute milers with their plates and purses in one hand, and holding their hats or hair nets on their heads with the other. I suppose it's fair to say my partner has the fittest and fastest bunch of customers in England! He will go to the utmost trouble looking after the old or sick, but tell him off for not waiting the week before and he'll probably tell you to get a lighter pair of running shoes!

We Acquire A Shop!

I started doing quite a bit of trade in the Bodmin area, a town well inland from St Austell, so it was only natural that when a butcher's shop became vacant at the end of our second year we took it over, to turn it into a wet fish shop. It made us independent of the co-op at Mevagissey and being only a few miles from Lostwithiel it was much handier for Jeff, also we had our own cold room, deep freezers, outbuildings etc.

At the time we took the shop over, fish prices started to go up. They have not so far come down again. Unfortunately wages did not keep pace with the rising prices and although we have kept our prices down as low as we dare, people just cannot afford nowadays to buy as much fish as they would like. Apart from the china clay industry centred around the St Austell area there are no major industries in our part of Cornwall. Bodmin is a fast developing town, with many new businesses and light industries just starting up, but it will be some time yet before people will have much money to spare to spend on fish, which many regard as a luxury.

When I opened the shop first I spent as much time telling customers how to cook their fish as I did serving them, as most of the young people had only bought frozen fish fingers or fillets before.

One bright young thing came in one day having spent a good while looking through the window at the display. "I've looked in several times but you never have that nice square yellow fish we buy in packets", she said.

I replied that it was probably smoked fish and showed her whole smoked haddocks, filleted smoked haddock, smoked haddock cutlets then cured cod fillets, but she showed not a glimmer of interest.

"No" she replied "We get ours in a cardboard box from the grocers, they're little square yellow fish!"

I politely tried to explain that fish weren't square and unless smoked were never yellow, but I felt I was losing ground fast.

Then it dawned on me, "Frozen fish in breadcrumbs" I blurted out triumphantly.

"Oh yes, it's frozen, but I didn't know it had breadcrumbs on it, I always thought it was the skin!"

I never did find out whether they were cod or haddock fillets, as she didn't know herself, but she's now quite an expert on fish I'm pleased to say, having become a regular customer. It's certainly an education serving the public. If you haven't tried it, you haven't lived; frustrating beyond belief at times, it makes you many friends and sometimes a few enemies, but on the whole it is a rewarding occupation.

Chapter 14

'We'll Try' and try again

PRICES of fish had been rising steadily ever since we started our business, and to make matters worse, the best quality fish was the scarcest and, of course, the dearest of all.

"I shall have to start up again and catch some" I said to Jeff one morning as we stood surveying a few boxes of poor quality, expensive fish we were supposed to make a profit from.

Jeff picked a very thin whiting from the top of a box and muttered horrible obscenities, both about the state of the whiting and the crafty so-and-so who had put it in the box, and charged us eighteen shillings a stone for it!

"I wish I were trawling now" I muttered, "I'll have to have a go".

Jeff by this time had seen enough of the fish, and heard enough of me nattering on, so he stomped off, to do his round, leaving me wondering if I ever should be able to get back to trawling and keep the shop open at the same time.

The following week Jeff told me that a boat called *We'll Try* was for sale up at Fowey. It sounded suitable for my requirements, so I went up and met the owner, a chap, I'd known before when he'd lived for a spell at Mevagissey. He told me he wanted to get a much larger boat and go trawling full time.

I sized the boat up and decided it was just the thing for inshore work. The outcome was that we decided to convert the boat for trawling and work it together. I was fortunate to get a young chap to take over the shop from me at the same time, so after a fortnight's holiday in August, hard labour was resumed in earnest.

The owner of the boat *We'll Try* was John Affleck, a gifted guitarist, banjo player, engineer and fisherman, who had settled in Cornwall to pursue what he liked doing, which was fishing and angling. He had already converted the thirty foot seiner into an excellent angling boat by taking away all but the for'ard deck, rehatching it at water level and building a real snazzy wheelhouse for'ard. The boat was powered by a forty horse Petter diesel, situated centrally aft and covered by a slightly raised engine box which served as a jolly good seat back there as well.

John had thought he had run the bearings previously to my first meeting with him about the boat, but he had later found the crank shaft was also damaged.

We decided to start from scratch and rebuild the engine. What a job it turned out to be! Although John lived at the little river village of Golant, the boat was moored a mile or more down the river in a pool which allowed it to remain afloat whatever the state of the tide. To get down there meant a good walk along the railway-track which served the docks at Fowey, then a short trip by punt to the boat. If we had anything heavy to take aboard or ashore we had to carry this by small boat up and down the river with the tide.

Black as crows, we sweated and swore our way through the slow process of rebuilding. I am not a mechanic, so was delegated to scraping, cleaning, de-gunging, painting, etc., everything John could lay his hands on.

Eventually we managed to get it finished and turned our attentions to the rest of it. John had seen a derelict boat lying at Padstow which had a nice trawl winch on its deck. I knew of it, but also knew the owner and I did not expect him to part with it, but to humour John more than anything else I went over with him to see if we could purchase it.

The boat in question was owned by a very hard working chap called Ian Lindley. He had done well as a fisherman, although originally he had been farming in Sussex. Ian had hit on the bright idea of running fish and shell fish direct to France, and through sheer determination and by hard work had built up a very sound business based at Padstow. He already had a small trawler he worked in what he called his "spare time" and had bought the old fifty foot trawler to do up at his leisure, but such was his capacity for hard work he never had any, so the old boat just lay there quietly rotting away.

I was very surprised when he agreed to sell the winch to us, as he had had many enquiries for it previously, anyway we were fortunate.

I sized the job up mentally, and asked Ian whether there was a mobile crane around to lift the winch off onto the quay.

"There's no crane here" he told me cheerfully.

"Don't worry Stan, I'll come down when you're ready and pull it up with one of my large vans!" Knowing Ian, who was I to argue!

Battle With the Winch

John and I arrived next day with a lethal selection of large hammers, chisels and spanners to do battle with the winch. It was a battle too. The deck was so rotten we had to lay old pieces of plank down wherever we wanted to stand, and of course the only sound part was where the winch stood. Coor!

We hammered, chiselled, levered, sweated and strained all the day. There was no way of taking it to pieces there and then so the whole lot, base plate and all had to come off, and thanks to John's ingenuity and perseverance eventually it did, but not before I had been down several times to fish our spanners out of three foot of oily bilge water when they had flown off rusted nuts to plunge into the dark chasm below!

A new Ford transit van careered round to the quay just as we finished levering the ironmongery clean of the woodwork.

Ian's genial face beamed down from above, "If you chaps are ready I'll nip off for some planks and a rope—shan't be a minute".

I was not happy. The tide was nearly full and we were still a good nine feet from the top of the quay, but there it was, it had to go up somehow!

I muttered subversive comments to John who wisely kept quiet. He's a wise old boy, John; I might be if I live long enough.

Anyway, back came Ian with the largest coil of thick polythene rope I'd seen for years, and a great pile of thick wide, long planks.

We levered the winch round to face the quay, put the ends of three planks under the winch bed as we tilted it back, then tied the rope to each foot of it. Ian brought the van back as far as he could without coming down aboard with us, then tied the rope to the bars that held the bumper on.

I couldn't contain myself any longer. "You'll pull the bumper off", I said.

"Well, we'll try it on there first, then if it does, I'll tie it round the axle" he replied cheerfully.

Such was his confidence I momentarily expected the winch to catapult up onto the quay like a toboggan at the end of its run! This train of thought was rudely interrupted by a loud bang as the bumper came off and the winch remained stationary!

Ian backed up again, then tied the rope to the axle. This time I expected to see the van drive off leaving the axle and back wheels behind, but instead the winch and planks leapt across the deck to hang halfway up the side of the quay. Stalemate!

Ian looked down hopefully, we looked up less hopefully, both of us taking care not to stand directly under our beloved machinery.

"I shall have to lower it again".

"Go easy or it'll go right through her" we hollered back in unison.

We threw some planks down where we hoped the winch would come to rest and waited. It came back down, the deck gave a bit then finally held.

By this time it was dark, so Ian hurriedly reversed back again, retied the rope and shouted "This time".

It nearly was for him! The rope took the full strain, then slipped off the axle. The van disappeared from our sight as if catapulted from the deck of an aircraft carrier.

The quay wasn't very wide, so when we heard a great screech of tyres not accompanied by a splash we knew he'd stopped in time, but only just, apparently!

The van backed again and a still smiling Ian reappeared.

"That was a close one, good job I had good brakes".

He disappeared in the darkness to tie the rope around the axle again.

This time the winch went up the wall to stick half way again. John and I joined Ian on the quay.

"Well, we've got it up halfway", says Ian.

John suggested we tried to lever it off the side of the quay with some of the great chunks of timber Ian had brought along.

In desperation I took a piece with John, got it down behind the base plate, then we pulled.

The ropes and van held firm and we found we could bounce the winch away from the wall a couple of feet.

"Hang on" said Ian. Being a big strong chap he seized an even larger piece of timber, and put it down on the other side of the plate to our piece.

"Now all together, pull" he shouted.

A Balancing Feat

I think we were all surprised when we found we had the winch up level with the quay sitting on the end of two great planks. Ian stood on his, John and I on ours.

The only snag was our plank was shorter than Ian's and if one of us stepped off to replace Ian so he could drive the van, our plank and the other chap left went up into space. So there we stood. Three men, two planks and a winch balanced on the end, five feet from the edge of the quay!

Fortunately we remembered there were two chaps working in a small yacht further along and after some frantic hollering they came and stood on Ian's plank while he pulled the winch into safety with the van.

The fact it wouldn't go through the door of the insulated body was a minor detail after that episode. We returned next day to dismantle it after another long struggle, and finally carted it away to John's place in my A35 van.

We made two journeys, it should have been three really, but the van just did it without collapsing, so we were very fortunate all round.

We had to get the outside of the drums reinforced before we put it aboard, also have a new base plate made. This gave me a chance to get the winch beds fitted while John got the rest of it in good condition.

Time glided away like the river we were spending so many weeks on. November came in sunny and warm, and by the middle of the month we had the winch installed and working. We had decided to put a gantry aft with another higher one behind the wheelhouse, which was also to hold a derrick centrally situated to plumb either side of the boat. Once again John's inventiveness came into play and we went hot foot to a steel tube depot in St Austell where we were able to get the whole range of pipes, T pieces, unions, stubs, curves, etc., which we needed, then we completed the job in a few days.

Once installed, we fitted stays, blocks and a roller, then we were ready for the big push. Or were we?

Sheets of net I had ordered at the beginning of August had not arrived, so I had two partly completed otter trawls and a seventeen foot six beam trawl we had made to experiment with as a side line. We put the beam trawl aboard, then a few days later broke the side off the starboard drum with the strain of lifting the sheer dead weight of the wretched thing. That finished beam trawling! It was not a success, but we had proved it to our satisfaction.

With the deep clear water we were working in plus the large quantities of rubbish about it was obvious from the start it would not be an economical proposition. Had we had a much larger boat with three times the power we might have done something.

Off came the winch drum again, then three weeks waiting until an engineer could fit the job in. We could have gone further afield and had the job done sooner, but the firm we chose had done several similar jobs before to another winch similar to ours, so we preferred to wait. I was able to complete our other gear during this spell, as well as do quite a bit of work on this book during the evenings in spite of a lot of help from my two children!

We eventually got going again in December and although fish was desperately scarce, we started to catch our share, which was very welcome for us and also for Jeff and Martin up at the shop. Christmas came, then the day after Boxing Day we went out and had a fine catch of mixed fish; then bad weather kept us in for a week. I went down with 'flu next, followed a week later by John. Not a very good start to the New Year, but there was worse to come.

Stranded—finally Salvaged

Bad weather persisted for a further week after we had shaken off the effects of our 'flu, then John arrived one Saturday morning to tell me the boat had broken her mooring chain and had grounded bow up on the top of the slipway adjacent to our moorings. I gathered up a couple of mates, then shot off to Golant in the van.

When we reached the boat my heart slid quietly into one of my sea boots. Almost vertical and laying on her side, decks facing down river, she appeared to be in an impossible position. Our only hope of refloating her was either to slide her bow down the slip until she was completely off it, or to strap enough buoyancy to her stern to float her off on the top of the tide.

Whatever happened we resigned ourselves to the fact that she would have to be submerged on the rising tide as time was all too short for us to do much that afternoon. We took out what equipment we could and tried levering her down the slip with some railway sleepers. We managed to shift the old lady a few feet and there she stuck.

I tied all the empty drums and cans I could lay my hands on around her quarters and tacked a great polythene sheet around her stern supported with fish boxes and planks from the inside. Then the tide ripped up the river. I knew in my mind she would not rise, and this was soon proved as the water rose above the sheet and poured into her again. There was nothing to do but go home and try again.

The following morning we made an early start. Armed with steel piping, crowbars and a good supply of hot drinks, we marched back for round two. When we had arrived she hadn't budged an inch, the only difference we could see as the tide started to leave the super-structure was that she was festooned with pieces of tree trunk and sea weed like a fully dressed Christmas-tree!

As soon as the water had gone down to enable us to stand sea boot deep at the bow, John and I levered away at it like a pair of madmen. We must have looked like a pair of ants toiling away, but like ants we got results. Slowly, a few inches at a time we were able to bounce her down the slip.

This was only made possible as the boat was ninety per cent submerged and in a state of semi-buoyancy, but when we had only a foot of her bow to get over the edge sheer weight defeated us, as by now the ebb tide had nearly left her again. There was no sense stopping though.

We hammered and levered away at the great granite stones forming the edge of the slip, managing to dislodge them, then roll them away clear.

Another frantic half hour's digging removed the rest of the slip below the bow then *We'll Try* slid hurriedly down onto the beach below.

Jeff, Martin and Stewart had turned up to help by this time, and when the tide made again we were ready for the final phase of the operation. The boat was still lying on her side down a very steep beach, so we had a variety of two, four and six part purchases attached to steel bars driven into the top of the river bank. One was attached to the top of the for'ard gantry, one to the gantry aft. We also had a steel cable attached to the port whipping drum of the winch leading to a cable puller on the bank.

We had borrowed a twenty-seven foot launch which we strapped to her port quarter, then with everyone at action stations we sat up and waited. This time all went according to plan, up she came with no trouble at all.

Although stranded in such an impossible position originally, she made only a tiny drop of water through a seam at water level on her port side.

Pleased and thoroughly exhausted, we towed her down to a fresh set of moorings kindly lent to us for the occasion and went home well satisfied.

As I write this, I have just returned from the boat where John and I have now finished getting everything back to working order again, a fortnight exactly since she broke a brand new galvanised mooring chain and did her balancing act on the slipway. Although *We'll Try* is her original name, I think under the circumstances it couldn't be better!

Chapter 15

Points on better marketing

As you will have read in the previous chapters, I, like most fishermen in Cornwall, have had to pursue all types of fishing at various times of the year. This was to take advantage of the availability of various species of fish and the existing demand for it, which unfortunately does not always coincide. A fisherman has also to take into consideration how to make the best use of his boat as well as the types of gear he has at his disposal. Only experience can give him all the answers. Even then, nature can play some funny tricks, and what may have been a lucrative fishery for many years, suddenly fails; but, usually, when one door shuts, another opens, and the fisherman turns to other types of fishing, which may perhaps have been unexploited or neglected for years, to find that results are even better than he ever dreamed of.

Sometimes a potential fishery exists, but there is only a limited local demand for that particular type of fish. If there are several chaps in the same community prepared to work together and co-operate, often a market is available, especially in the winter time, when fish of all sorts is generally scarce and highly priced. It pays to enquire, not just once, but all over the place, as to who might wish to handle the fish on a commission basis at a market or, better perhaps, buy it direct.

The same applies to transport. By enquiring thoroughly, often fish lorries delivering or collecting supplies can be found to call and collect fish, or fish can be sent by local transport to link up with a "trunker" road service to one of the major markets. Even boxes are no great problem. As those made of wood are highly priced and are now non-returnable by law, waxed cardboard boxes can be purchased in bulk, with your name, or the name and address of your group printed on them. (It pays to advertise, especially if your product is consistently in good condition and well graded.) These boxes, at the time of writing, cost around two shillings (ten new pence) each to hold two stone of fish plus ice. A stapler and staples are needed to clip the boxes together and you are in business. Larger boxes cost proportionately less per stone of fish.

I admit ice can be a tricky problem, especially if you are a long way from an ice works and there are not enough of you to warrant buying an ice making machine. If ice is available, although some distance away, and you have no cold room, it is worth considering building a large box, or small shed in which to keep it, and then having a lorry load at a time, using it as needed. Work out how much ice you need to store. Then when you have a rough idea of the size needed for your box or bin, build it either of wood, brick or block, whichever is handiest and cheapest. It should be sited in a shaded place, or in a cool shed. Either you can build the bin the exact size to hold a certain quantity of ice, or you can make it large enough to hold your stock of ice one end, and a supply of boxes or loose iced fish at the other, this, of course is only necessary if fishing is light or transport not always immediately available.

Ice can be kept either loose or in bags. Loose ice has to be dug out. This takes more time and raises the temperature of the bin, creating wastage; while bagged ice takes up more room, but is easier to handle. If it's frozen hard, a few hearty wallops with a shovel whilst it is still in the sack will quickly break it up again for use. It is important when constructing a storage bin for ice, to remember to slope the floor towards a small drainage hole, the smaller the better, as this should be the only break in the insulation. A hole of half inch diameter is all that is needed for a bin holding half a ton of ice, provided it is kept clear.

The insulation for the bin should be four inch thick expanded polystyrene. This can be purchased in two inch slabs with a special adhesive compound, to stick the sheets to the sides and top, also together, and can be obtained direct from a manufacturer or through a firm specialising in supplying large refrigeration equipment. Care should be taken to cut the sheets square and when one layer is stuck on, make sure to overlap all joints thoroughly with the second layer, especially at the corners. To make the base for a bin, get a level surface, pack a few inches of rubble down, then lay two inches of concrete on this and skim level on the top.

If you intend to build up more than four feet in any material heavier than wood, you should first dig footings for your walls, and place nine inches to a foot of concrete in a trench to take the weight and to avoid subsidence. The bin can have a flat top if under cover, or slightly sloping if situated outside. When the sides have been constructed, battening of four inch by two inch wood should be nailed inside to coincide with the ends of the thin gauge alloy sheets which are used to cover the four inches of insulation, then the insulation is stuck in between the battens. The job is then finally covered by the alloy

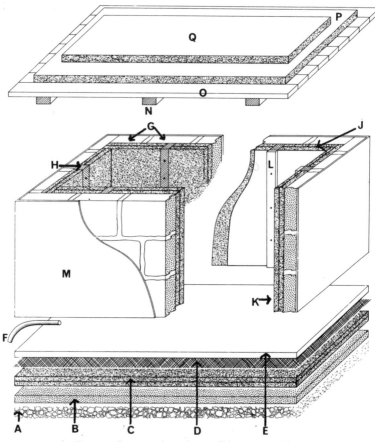

FIG. 1   Construction of a small ice storage bin

(a) 3–6 in. of rubble tightly packed   (b) 2 in. rough concrete, skimmed level
(c) one or two sheets of expanded polystyrene   (d) wire mesh
(e) 2 in. waterproofed concrete to slope towards drainpipe   (f) drainpipe
(g) concrete or clinker blocks
(h) 4 x 2 in. wooden battens nailed to wall
(j) two layers 2 in. expanded polystyrene sheeting
(k) alloy sheet nailed to 4 x 2 in. battens or held by 2 x $\frac{1}{2}$ in. battens to cover
     joins. Sheet to extend below floor level to a depth of at least 2 in.
(l) 2 x $\frac{1}{2}$ in. battens
(m) layer of plaster (cement and sand)
(n) 2 x 1 in. battens
(o) $\frac{5}{8}$ in. tongued and grooved planking screwed to battens. Make lid about 9 in.
     larger all round than top of bin to allow for ample coverage
(p) 2 in. polystyrene sheet to fit over whole exterior dimensions of bin
(q) second layer of 2 in. polystyrene to fit into interior dimensions of bin
     To allow shedding of rainwater, a flat false top can be made to slope to the
back of the bin, by using a piece of 4 x 2 in. on the front edge, and covering the
whole with roofing felt.

sheeting, which should go right down to the first layer of concrete on the floor.

Two or, better still, four inches of expanded polystyrene can be laid on the floor, some diamond mesh reinforcing laid on that, then the final layer of two inches of cement skimmed off and sloped down to the corner you wish to drain the bin from. If you can get some frost proofer to mix in the last floor layer it will stop it cracking later.

For a quick job, stick the insulation all round, put a few inches of metal above and below the concrete floor to stop the drainage seeping into the insulation; lean some old hardboard or similar material against the sides and that's that. The lid can be made of wood.

Stick on two inches of insulation all over the underside, then mark the inside area of the lid and stick on a further two inches to fit down inside the bin. The lid should lift straight on and off and can be held down by hooks and eyes or something similar.

When the floor has set properly, cut a small hole out through at the lowest point, fit a tube in for drainage and cement around it; if you wish, you can then plaster the outside!

A cold room is constructed on much the same lines, with the exception of the floor, where a special sort of insulation material is used under the concrete, which has to be thicker to stand much more weight than a small ice bin. Any firm selling commercial refrigeration equipment will be pleased to advise you on the construction of a cold room with a view to future business should you require equipment at a later stage.

If you should contemplate building a cold store, it is advisable to get several firms to give you quotations for materials and machinery. It is surprising how much these can vary and how competitive the business is, especially if you are not in a hurry, or give that impression! It is also advisable to remember that fish is not generally stacked up more than four or five feet high, so that it is not necessary to build a cold room any higher than is needed to put the door frame in securely. These doors are specially made, and it is essential to have a proper one otherwise a greater amount of cooling will be needed and consequently running costs will be considerably higher.

An ice storage bin, be it ever so humble, can be utilized to hold extra ice or fish even after a cold room is built, should the space be needed. We have a 1,500 cubic foot cold room at Mevagissey and are now contemplating installing an ice making machine which we are hoping can be installed on the end of the cold room outside, and high enough to gravity feed the ice directly into the cold room to a storage pound there, or perhaps into a bin constructed in a similar way as the one I have just outlined.

Gutting, washing and icing fish should be done as soon as possible after catching. Great care should be taken at all times when handling fish, to avoid crushing and bruising, this can easily happen if too many are put into a box or basket when landing. It doesn't take much longer to handle fish carefully, and it must be remembered that fish start to deteriorate as soon as they are caught, so the quicker they can be cleaned and cooled off, the better their condition when they are offered for sale in a fish shop. The person who eats that fish is the person we depend upon for a living. Fish should always be placed neatly into a box, leaving ample room for a shovel of ice to go on top and not crush the fish when the lid is placed on and the boxes stacked. Small, granulated or flake ice is the best for the job, as it melts quickly and the resulting water trickles down through the fish cooling it in a comparatively short time. Another advantage of small ice is that a layer can be put between fish to accelerate the chilling process without damaging it, which did happen with the larger lumps from the old fashioned ice plants.

It is quite a good idea to put a layer of ice between fish if they are being kept or sent away in large bins or cases.

Care and common sense used in the handling of fish can be worth a lot more than most people imagine, often making the difference between an uneconomical price and a very good one.

Chapter *16*

How to mend, handle and shoot nets and trawls

I'M always keen to learn of new and different methods of fishing, so perhaps it may be of interest to describe in detail some of the gear and the methods used around our Cornish coasts. If these are not entirely suitable to other areas, they may give the beginner something to think about which he can adapt for his own specific needs in his part of the country.

When I first started fishing I imagined every fisherman could mend a net. I was surprised to find that quite a few of them couldn't and when it came to stepping-in and replacing pieces, breeding, tapering and cutting, many were completely lost. So I made it my business to learn as much as possible. It took me a long time, I made many mistakes, but now I'm a moderately good hand at it, so before waffling on about different sorts of nets, I'll try to give the beginner a rough idea of their construction and how to mend them.

The nicest description of a net I've ever heard is "A lot of holes joined together by string!" Of course, most nets today are manufactured of synthetic yarns, which are not quite so easy to mend properly as knots tend to slip. Plenty of care and much practice are the best answers to this trouble. If you are to attempt to mend a small mesh net, don't have too large a needle to start with, and don't try to fill it up to capacity with twine. This will make it difficult to work through the meshes—and you will have enough fingers and thumbs getting in the way to start off with without that!

Obtain a sharp, small bladed pen knife for trimming net, then get away quiet somewhere with a good light, so you can concentrate on the job in hand and have a good swear if you feel like it! There's nothing worse than having an audience when you're trying to mend a net and you are only a beginner. The funny thing is, as soon as you are proficient, no one will take the slightest notice of you!

Nets are made to hang a "right" way. If the net is a small one already roped to a headline, look at the way the knots are constructed and how the net hangs from top to bottom. All the meshes will close up completely if gathered in squarely from side to side, and the knots will be seen to lay in neat rows. Turn the net round the other way and it will be seen to be springy and the knots will not lay together neatly at all.

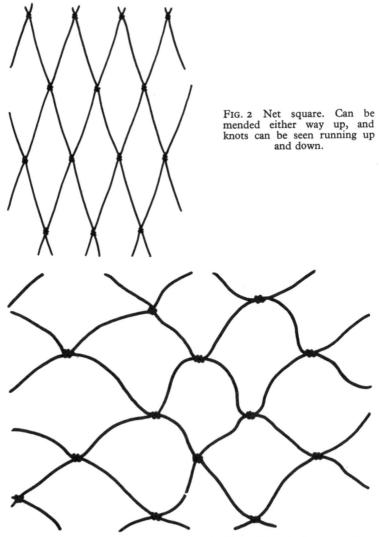

FIG. 2 Net square. Can be mended either way up, and knots can be seen running up and down.

FIG. 3 Net wrong way up for mending. In this position the knots run from side to side and net does not lay evenly, mesh for mesh, knot for knot.

The same applies if you hold a piece of net up square one way, then the other. You will see the meshes hang either as perfect diamonds or will be looking as though they are pulled the wrong way.

On Mending A Hole

We'll assume you have a small hole to mend. Get the net square as in Fig. 2 and gather plenty of net together squarely, directly above the hole and at least three feet from it. Tie this together and slip a large hook through the gathered up meshes and fix it to something about eye level.

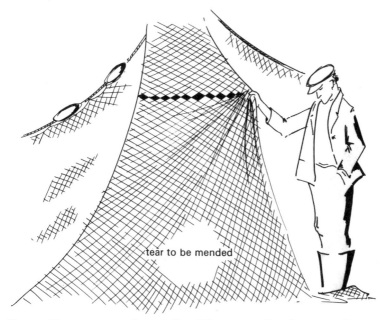

tear to be mended

FIG. 4   To prepare a net for mending, follow a row of meshes across the net, gathering them in evenly. Leave at least three feet of netting between hook and tear.

Find the hole again, then at the top of it cut away one mesh leaving a bar. It does not matter which side of the hole you start from, so long as it is in the very top row of meshes, Fig. 6.

Often a bar can be seen already to start on without having to cut a mesh. If the net is of synthetic material, do not trim the loose ends right back to the side knots, as if any strain is put on the net the knots will slip, creating more mending.

Start on Bar A. Then, going from left to right, make a mesh round your finger and come up to point B, down to C with a side knot then

FIG. 5   Correct position of repair in relation to hook.

from right to left to D, E, down to a side knot F then to G, H, down to a side knot I then to J, K then to a side knot L, then down again to M, where you start to pick up your bottom points or meshes.

In Cornwall this is known as picking up your underhand meshes, and if you do not watch carefully for these you will find that you will have to do an extra row for your carelessness and cut out the mesh on the way back again.

From M continue to N, O (another underhand point), up to P, then down to another bar Q to finish off on.

I have been able to teach a couple of people to mend nets quickly by using a blackboard and coloured chalks. Get a straight edge and draw a net on the board. Take a damp cloth and rub a hole in it. I know it sounds strange, but it does work. Then, with your fingers, rub out the net to leave it with a bar at the top, top points, side meshes and underhand points, making sure that you have a bar to finish on.

If you haven't, you have gone wrong somewhere, so start at the beginning and check again.

Take a coloured chalk and draw in a row just as if you are using twine. When you reach your first side knot, use a different coloured chalk for the second row, and so on until you finish off. See Figs. 7 and 8.

To mend a tear that does not have any net missing or only a few meshes, gather up the net squarely as in Figs. 4 and 5 again, directly above the tear at its highest point in the net, but always tie or hook it at least three feet from where you intend to start mending.

FIG. 6   Mending sequence, starting at A and finishing on Q.

It does not matter whether the tear runs up and down, diagonally or sideways, the net must always be hung squarely and well gathered in to mend it. The procedure is the same as for a hole: Fig. 9.

Start at the highest point of the tear, always on a bar, remembering to pick up the underhand points when they occur on either side of the rip and again finishing on a bar.

If you don't and you started on a bar correctly, you will have missed a mesh or made an extra one somewhere. Check back through your work and cut out again from where you made your mistake; it's all practice.

If you have a rip running across a net, and it is any length, then is the only time it is practical to turn the net round. See Fig. 10. especially if you are in a hurry to repair it. By doing this, you only have a few points to contend with, there being nearly all side knots as the net is turned to hang from A instead of B.

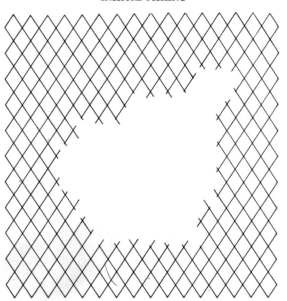

FIG. 7   Chalk drawing of net rubbed out to make hole.

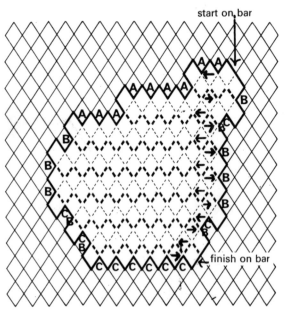

FIG. 8   Filling in the chalk drawing.
(a) top points   (b) side knots   (c) underhand points

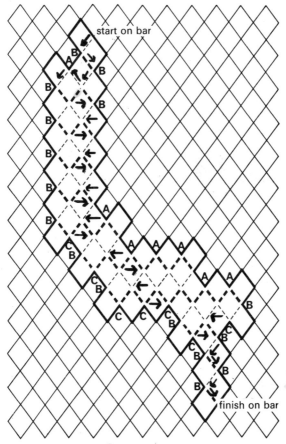

FIG. 9 Cutting out and mending a rip.
(a) top points   (b) side knots   (c) underhand points

If a piece of net is missing, count the number of meshes across and down that will give you a clearly cut square or rectangle clear of any damage, then cut out as in Fig. 11. You will see that the net has a rectangular hole thirteen points wide and four side knots deep. Note that when sewing in a piece of net, *NO BAR* is used to start on. The piece of net to sew in is one mesh less each way. Start at A sew across to B, then down to C, across to D then finish there and start again at A, sewing down to join at D.

If a net is very badly damaged in one section, it is often quicker to cut right down the net along a row of side knots, down each side of the damaged area, and completely remove the section. You then sew

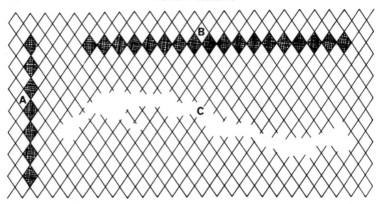

FIG. 10   A: skim straight up the meshes to gather, then mend in normal way.
B: normal gathering direction, i.e., across meshes. C: tear across net.

down from top to bottom using side knots all the way, but make sure
that you leave a bar at the top of one side of the net, otherwise you
will find you are a row of meshes out either at the top or bottom of
one side of your net, see Figs. 12 and 13.

Cut the headrope at the centre of the damaged area, unless it is a
long piece of net you are removing. You will need a couple of feet of
headline each side to either splice together when sewing down is
completed, or to tie together.

It is advisable to tie the ends of your rope down after knotting, so
they will not catch up in the net when shooting it.

There are excellent books that include rope and wire splicing,
also net making and setting, which are obtainable from Fishing News

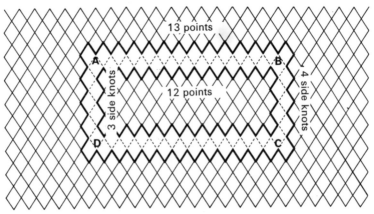

FIG. 11   Damaged net cut for repair.

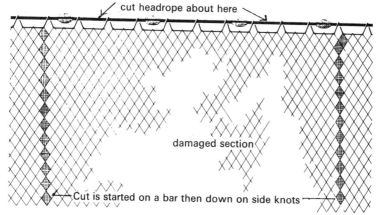

FIG. 12   Cutting out a damaged section.

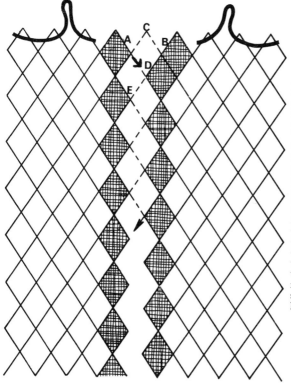

FIG. 13   The damaged section having been correctly cut out, the two pieces of net will look like this. To commence the join, hang from meshes A and B. Starting at knot B, leave plenty of twine to complete mesh C to A. From A go across and down to D then E, etc. Complete mesh C when net is taken down, and then join head-ropes, making sure the net hangs slack at the join.

(Books) Ltd., of 110 Fleet Street, London, EC4, so I will not go into these subjects, which have been dealt with far better already than I am able to do.

If you are not happy about your ability to splice, a good knot is a lot better than a bad splice, unless of course you are dealing with wire.

Know Your Knots

There are two basic knots you will need for mending nets, and these are illustrated in Figs. 14 to 19 inclusive. Don't be afraid to use double knots if things look "slippery"! Don't worry if you have a few ends hanging about if you are working on synthetic material, or if your work looks untidy if you are a beginner. Do make sure that the meshes and bars you make and breed are not smaller than the original net, as this will restrict the area around the mending. This is quite easy to avoid—the answer is keep trying, if you do get stuck and really frustrated, put it down and have another go the next day. It's surprising how a fresh start will solve a problem, and if you do know anyone who mends nets, don't be hesitant about asking them to help you, as most people are only too glad to do so if approached in the proper manner.

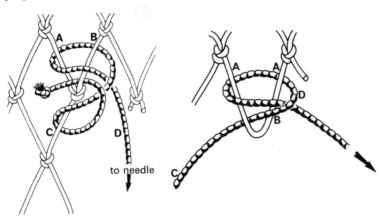

FIG. 14 (*Left*) Method of fastening mending twine to bar when commencing repair. An overhand knot at the end of the twine prevents slipping, especially when using synthetic materials. The new knot grips each side of the knot formed by bars A, B and C, thus preventing the mending twine D from slipping up or down bar B and C.

FIG. 15 (*Right*) Breeding from left to right to join a side mesh to a top point or breeding a row of meshes across from point to point. The needle is passed up and into the back of mesh A, passed out at B and pulled to the required length at C. B is then pinched between finger and thumb while a large loop is made of the twine D. The needle is then passed round the back of mesh A, through loop D, which is tightened as in Figure 14 until jammed.

Very often at certain times of the year, for instance during November at Mevagissey, we have shoals of herring which come right in shore. So close in fact that a boat could not drift for them in the normal

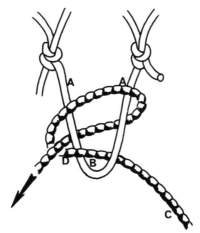

FIG. 16   The same procedure is adopted as in Figure 15 when breeding to point from right to left.

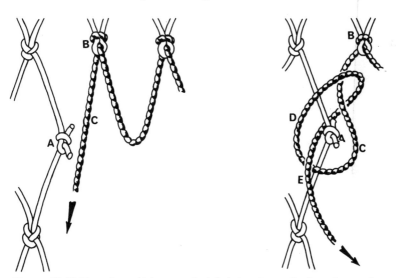

FIG. 17 (*Left*) To make a sideknot on the left, bring the needle down from point B and then pinch C to A with finger and thumb, making sure length of twine is correct from C to A. (*Right*) Throw a large loop with twine C to D, passing needle around back of knot A and out through at E, then pull very tight and release fingers, making sure the side knot is encircled by the new knot.

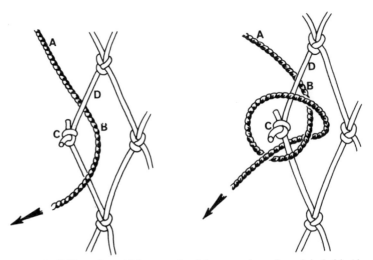

FIG. 18 (*Left*) To make a sideknot on the right, come down from A in behind bar D, and again pinch B and C with the finger and thumb. (*Right*) Throw a loop as before, passing needle in through back of knot C.

manner. Then we use "bay nets" or anchored nets. For anyone thinking of using this method, good secondhand herring nets can be bought very reasonably now. Try to get East coast nets which have a headrope and a footrope attached. Then split them lengthwise, taking the bottom half of the net, and inserting corks in the footrope and joining A to B. This will give you twice the length of net which will be deep enough for your needs. See Fig. 20.

It is advisable to join several nets together by sewing down on the straight run of diamonds, but if you are in a hurry, see Fig. 21.

Tie headropes together, make sure A and B are level and seize the nets squarely at intervals from top to bottom. A series of half hitches with a needle in light cotton will be ample for this task.

Art of Shooting Nets

There are many factors which govern where and how many anchored nets can be shot at a time, depending on depth of water, run of tide and the nature of the bottom. If there is a good depth of water it will not matter if the bottom is a bit rough, but always try to shoot your nets over mud or sand to avoid damaging them should they sweep or go down with the pull of tide or weight of fish.

As you will see in Fig. 22 the anchor is first shot with a good rope coming up to buffs and a dahn on the surface. The nets are attached to

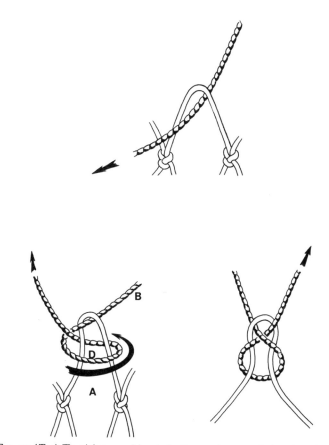

FIG. 19 (*Top*) To pick up and knot a bottom point or underhand mesh, come in through from behind, then pinch twine B at point C as before. (*Bottom left*) Pull tight and release fingers. (*Bottom right*) This knot has been made in the same manner, but the point has been picked up from left to right.

rope A and the other end to rope B, which should be long enough to haul the dahn rope tight to reach the connecting rope. Then when point C is reached, the net can be skimmed up and pulled over the boat and down the other side while unmeshing takes place without hauling up the anchors and reshooting. If your boat is too large to do this, then a strap can hold the boat either stern or bow onto the

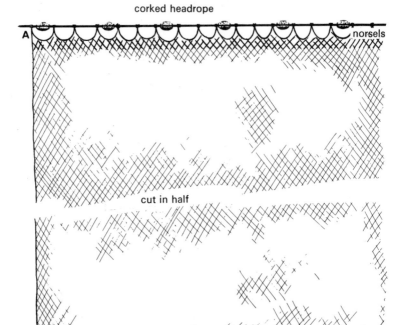

FIG. 20   Cutting a deep net.

nets; or in fine weather a metal hook attached by a short rope to the boat and passed between the two headlines and jammed against a cork will suffice to hold her steady.

Always shoot the nets with the tide, and try to work them against the tide, unless the wind is stronger. The coble straps D fixed to the nets at E and F need to be one, two or three fathoms in length, depending on whether there is a likelihood of boats passing over them. It is always advisable to have at least one fathom of strap on them so a boat drawing up to six feet can pass over them. The cobles can be made up of corks, or small plastic buffs can now be obtained. A good idea is to get some plastic balls and put net round them to fasten them to the strap.

Herrings come right in against the beaches and cliffs here at Mevagissey

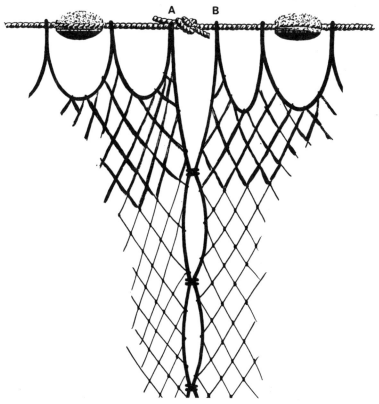

FIG. 21 A quick method of joining two pieces of netting.

before they spawn, and the closer in you can shoot your gear the better, but if out winds are forecast, bring your gear in rather than take a chance. It pays in the long run. Nets can be shot in the afternoon, then hauled and carried in again later that night if there is any doubt about the weather.

If you are in an area where herring put in only a brief appearance, a few anchor nets may well be worth while. We find three eighty yard nets enough to anchor in a string if there is any tide running, but in a shallow bay you can put out ten times as many if there is only a gentle flow of tide in and out against the shore.

In Cornwall, the average length herring or pilchard net is one hundred and twenty yards long before setting. After setting to a headrope it is around seventy-four yards long. East Coast nets being

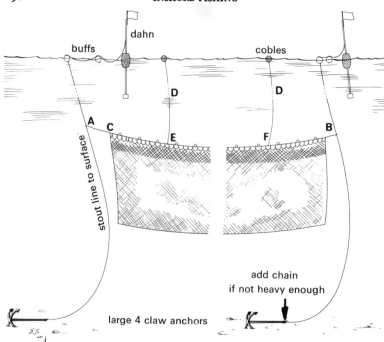

FIG. 22 Anchored bay net.

shorter require three sewed together to make the length of one and a quarter Cornish nets.

If you require to reset a net of this type, measure the length of twenty-two complete meshes along the bottom of your net, making

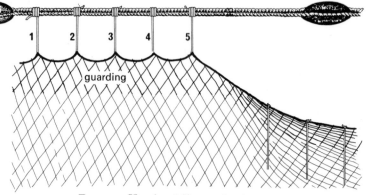

FIG. 23a Hanging driftnet to headropes.

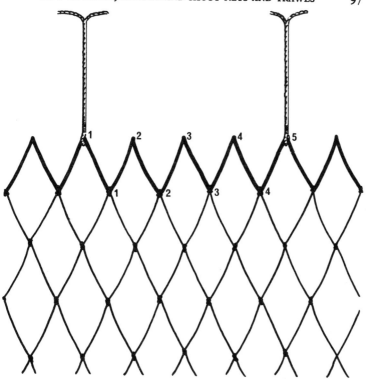

FIG. 23b   Norsels on a herring net are hung every fifth point.

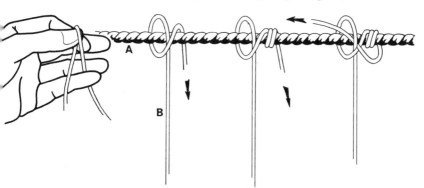

FIG. 24   A norsel hitch to headropes. A: Main line; B: to net.

sure they are completely square. Mark the exact length on a stick, then mark your headrope with chalk, the exact length of the twenty-two meshes.

Hang the five norsels as shown in Fig. 23a and attach with a norsel hitch as in Fig. 24.

If the norsels 1 and 5 are tied correctly to the marks, norsel 3 can be hung by "eye" in the centre, then 2 and 4 spaced between. Fig. 23b.

It is interesting to note that full sized herring or pilchard drift nets always have two headropes held together by the norselling. One rope is a left-handed lay, the other right-handed. This stops the ropes, and therefore the net, twisting up when any strain is put on the head-ropes, as one turns against the other.

If you cut a net long to make several very shallow nets, the strain will be considerably less, so a small, well stretched, single headrope will suffice.

There are several rows of heavy mesh reinforcing at the top of a drift net called guarding down here in Cornwall; if the net has a footrope as well, guarding will be found along the bottom of the net also; therefore if you intend to cut your net along in three sections, the centre one will be without guarding, so you should sew along the top row of points with stouter twine, knot for knot, as reinforcing from which you can hang your norsels. These should be hung from every fifth mesh and floats slid on as you tie your norsels up.

Nylon Gill and Tangle Nets are another form of anchored net fishing that has really "caught on" in the last few years in Cornwall and may prove a very useful addition to an inshore fisherman's income at certain times of the year wherever he may work from, especially if he can work an area of rocky or stony ground undisturbed by trawlers or escallop dredgers.

Again, there is an excellent book on the subject published by Fishing News (Books) Ltd., and written by John Burgess,* so I will not go into too much detail, but will attempt to describe how the use of very fine synthetic nets has improved fishing here in Cornwall, especially in the spring of the year.

Success of New Nylon Nets

Trammel and crab nets have always been used to good effect around the Cornish Coasts, catching crab, occasional lobsters, crayfish, ray, turbot and angler fish, known in the trade as "monk tails" but having nothing to do with the monk or angel fish! The headlines were floated with pieces of flat cork, which after being shot a couple of times in deep water became water logged and the nets had to be hung up to dry out the cork again. The corks also being odd sizes caught in the nets as they were being shot, as did the barrel leads used to keep the foot rope down. The nets were constructed of thick cotton and some-times hemp twine, which was heavily cured in tar and cutch to stop

Fishing Boats and Equipment

them rotting and to cut down on the amount of abrasion and tearing this type of fishing produces on the gear.

With the introduction of the nylon gill net, much larger catches of bass, pollock and mullet were taken, and a few people tried a shallow larger mesh net anchored on the bottom, to see how it would work. Results were astonishing to say the least.

Several small boats here, whose owners just shot the nets in the hope of catching a few crabs in and around the bay, started landing cod, large pollock, rays, turbot, angler fish, large lobsters etc., etc., in quite good quantities. Those fish that did not mesh properly were found nicely tangled up in the fine soft meshes, and so the nets had come to stay.

Fishermen in other ports were quick to realise the advantages of these nets and large catches of crayfish started coming in, being caught by this method of fishing. As they are so fine, the nets do suffer considerable damage, but pay for themselves so quickly, that it is more economical to cut them off the head and foot rope when they get too badly worn and to replace them with new netting, than to spend many weeks mending them.

It is far better to set up the netting on the head and footropes yourself, as by this means considerable saving can be achieved over buying the nets already set up. The nets I have just mentioned are a single sheet, with no "trencher" mesh, that is a larger mesh hung on one or both sides of a much smaller mesh. The fish hits this smaller mesh and then swims on through a larger mesh to find he has "bagged" himself up. With the fine nets, a trencher mesh does not appear necessary, as it requires a lot of extra work making and setting this to the main sheet of net. But if you have any doubts in the matter it would be wise to compare the performance of a few of each type of net before setting up too many.

The cork floats have now been superseded by streamlined plastic floats, which do not absorb water, therefore the nets are easier to handle and do not require drying. A braided, lead-cored footrope is now being marketed, which does away with the small barrel leads. It is fairly expensive compared with the old method of making up a footline, but the ease of working and attaching it should make it a proposition if you are in an area where your nets are paying off well.

I have used the term anchor nets, but as there is so little resistance to tide compared with the older types of nets, a good lump of chain or scrap iron is quite suitable to use instead of an anchor. It is also advisable to tie a small piece of chain along the footrope at intervals as an addition to the weighted foot, to stop the nets sweeping and rolling, especially if there is any "ground" sea where they are shot.

Gill nets are often shot to good effect along the edge of an area of rocky ground as the fish inhabiting such terrain often move off on to smoother bottom at night to return at daylight.

Tangle nets can also be shot to advantage in the same sort of area, and of course, over patchy or stony ground.

Angler fish tails, ray, turbot and all kinds of shellfish are much in demand today, so perhaps a few nets such as I have described may prove to be a proposition on a small or large scale, depending on where you may work from.

Traps and Pots for Shellfish

Shell fishing or "potting" as we call it is another subject which has been written about in detail by people far more qualified than myself.

There is one interesting idea though, which has been produced by a firm at Porthleven in Cornwall. This consists of a trap made on the Welsh creel style, but rectangular, with a square, strongly constructed wire mouth, which has a wire flap to completely close the mouth from the inside. This is hinged and held back by a wire staple which is secured against the strain of a strong rubber band by a peg type time fuse. These fuses disintegrate by electrolytic action, closing the mouth of the trap very securely. Fuses of six—twelve—eighteen hours duration are available, and this new development could be a boon to a lobster fisherman, especially when he is unable to haul his gear regularly.

There are many different types of trap and pot being used around Cornwall today. I can remember long bitter arguments going on between the old men here when a younger crabber made some wire pots to try out. To the old men it was heresy! But as results proved, they wore better, caught more lobsters and were lighter to work. Since then, all sorts of pots and traps have been tried out and many adopted, it being mainly a matter of personal preference which type is used.

One subject which has been constantly under discussion, often very heatedly, for several years now here in Cornwall, has been the effect of skin diving on the stocks of shellfish and the results achieved by traditional methods. Many of the older men engaged in shell fishing by these traditional methods are dead against it, and quite rightly so, as they have had catches removed from their gear by unscrupulous persons, and this amounts to plain thieving, but which it is almost impossible to prove in a court of law.

The younger shell fisherman who fishes by traditional methods is in most cases, more tolerant of the skin diver, as he knows it is a dangerous occupation and if great care is not exercised permanent physical harm can result after a season or two at it. I know of some young skin divers who are only using this method of fishing as a

means to an end, as they intend to save enough to purchase and equip
their own boats so they can follow traditional methods of fishing after
a few years diving.

The fuss will die down in time; whether it is harmful to stocks or
not I am not qualified to say. If a skin diver does not interfere with
other people's gear and catches, good luck to him I say, but if he
makes his pile emptying pots and traps, may I wish him a hearty
attack of the bends! To those who run down the skin diver just because
he is one, let them try it, after all the risks have been fully explained
to them. It must also be remembered that the minority usually spoil
something for the majority, as in the case of thieving from traps.
Most legitimate skin divers are as honest as the traditional fishermen,
but there are always exceptions on either side. I sincerely hope that
the skin diver will eventually be accepted in fishing communities as
were other innovations in the past. It is a terrible thing to see men at
loggerheads, especially when their livelihoods are involved. Already
common sense is prevailing in most communities over this matter.
I sincerely hope it continues, as no doubt the arguments for and
against will persist for several years yet.

Long Lining and Boultering

This method of fishing as you will have read in previous chapters,
provides fishermen in Cornwall with a good living at certain times of
the year, usually late spring, summer and autumn. The larger boats
work right through these periods while the smaller ones use this type of
fishing as a "stop gap" in the spring and autumn.

Big boats equipped with either hydraulic or motor line haulers use
six or even nine thread sisal lines as main lines, with staple nylon
stops taking the place of the sixteen ounce hemp lines which incidentally
were also used for the main line of a whiting spilter. Hooks used at
Mevagissey are Allcocks No. 5 swivel hook; further west, larger
hooks are used. See Fig. 25a.

It is interesting to note that if you intend to work line in an area
where a lot of ground swell exists, the swivel hooks have a tendency
for the hook to wash out of the swivel, and unless a patent type of
hook with a spring swivel bedding into a recessed channel cut around
the top of the hook shank is used, it is better to use eyed hooks, tied
straight to the stops.

Long line stops are set on the main line seven feet apart, giving
around three feet two inches for the length of stop. A clove hitch is
used to tie the hook to the stop, while a norsel hitch is used to tie the
stop to the main line. You will notice the stop is doubled back each
end where it is tied, Fig. 25b. This makes the stop "Stand off" the
main line better and of course wears much longer where tied.

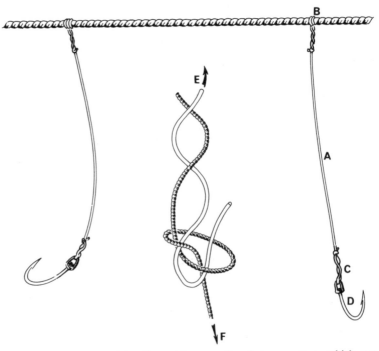

FIG. 25a   A section of longline with seven feet between stops, which are 38 ins. long. The main line is of six or nine thread sisal. A: stops; hemp or staple nylon. B: norsel hitch. C: clove hitch. D: No. 5 Allcocks swivel hook.

FIG. 25b (*Inset*)   Method of twisting back longline stop after fastening to main line or hook swivel. E: Knot on hook or main line; F: to hook or main line.

A line for a smaller boat should be of manilla or sisal about five-eighths of an inch circumference if to be hauled by hand, the stops being placed on the main line as far apart or as close as you require, depending whether you wish to cover a small area with a large number of hooks or cover a lot more ground with the same number. You should be careful when setting up line not to put your stops on too closely, so that when the main line is stretched fully and two stops pulled in towards each other the hooks cannot catch. This is a nuisance when hauling and clearing line. For inshore fishing we prefer to have our hooks closer together than for deep water longlining.

A wide, flat bottomed cane basket is the best container from which to work line. Strips of cork are tied around the top to stick the hooks in, and a few feet of line is left out and half hitched to the rim when you first start coiling line into an empty basket.

This line will be the bottom one of your basket of line and needs to be left out to tie onto the top of your next basket as you shoot. Make sure it is up clear of the basket and not passed through the cane when you tie it to the next one, or you'll have to shoot basket and all!

When about twenty hooks have been stuck around into the cork in a clockwise direction, the stops are bunched, then pulled through a gap between the canes of the basket. This allows the hooks to be pulled out for baiting, and is very important, as if not done, the weight of a full basket of line will not allow a hook to be pulled out at all, thus making it almost impossible to bait the last hooks and hang them over the side, see Fig. 26.

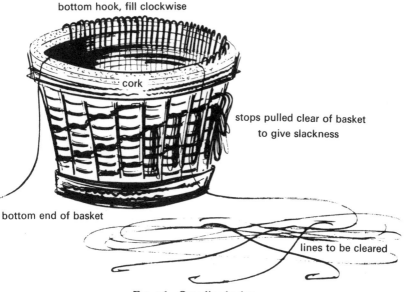

FIG. 26   Cane line basket.

Lines can be purchased cured, but after being used for a while it is advisable to boil them in cutch, especially before drying and storing the gear. Whenever long line hooks are replaced around a basket, it is advisable to brush on a small quantity of lubricating or heavy fish oil over the curves of the hooks just above the points. This will stop the hooks from rusting and make them much easier to bait next time, but care should be taken not to allow the oil to run down the shank of the hook, as it will weaken the stop, especially if hemp or cotton is used. Lastly, remember that when clearing line, it is advisable to carry a spare, corked basket; then, when the first basket has been hauled, one hand can clear from that one into the empty one, if you have enough labour, or the chap working the boat can do it when he has had a bit of practice.

To clear a basket of line into its own basket, first push all projecting hooks back into the line through the sides of the basket. Place a lid or folded oilskin over the top, then tip the basket over. Turn the pile of line back again, then commence clearing. The same system applies with spilter. *Remember to turn the line twice, or you'll be all day picking out hooks from "in under"*.

When the basket is to be baited, the bottom hook is started on first, working around to the top one. It is always a good idea to check that the last hook is the last or top hook, then to leave it baited laying on the top of the line. By doing this, if you are looking for the top end of the line in a hurry, it can be easily found by taking the baited hook and running your hands a few feet along the main line either way.

We use pilchard, mackerel or squid for line bait; on the North coast around St Ives, sand eels are seined for bait, and are excellent for catching rays. Whereas we use our bait cut up to convenient sizes, sand eels are used whole, more than one being used if small.

If you intend to shoot line across an estuary or sandy area, where the ground is relatively small but prolific in ray for instance, zig zag the line across and back over the ground when you shoot; at each change of direction, pull the line tight before turning, and tie a bunch of chain to the main line; then commence shooting in the new direction.

When shooting line, always throw the line away at right angles to the boat, or even slightly forward of that. Never let your arm come around behind you as you throw or you will find stops and hooks coming back over the rail. There is also a tendency to twist the stops and baits around the main line when throwing round like this. Keep a sharp knife handy at your side and in the stern of the boat when shooting. Never panic—and try to think ahead of trouble.

Some Helpful Hints

If you have a few hooks tangled in a bunch, shoot it and then untangle it when you haul.

If in doubt, cut, especially if you have to stop shooting for any reason such as motor trouble etc. Always have a dhan line with anchor or weight tied on ready with buffs and a dahn on the other end. Tie the cut line to the anchor and shoot away the dahn line. It can always be hauled up and shooting recommenced afterwards.

Line should always be shot across or with the tide, and hauled with the tide whenever possible unless on "hitchy" ground in shallow water. Then it will be found easier to haul against the tide, or at least easier to work the gear in without sweeping and hitching so much.

Three times the depth of water being fished is the length for the dahn lines, which should have one or two large buffs or buoys tied near the top end to take the strain off of the dahn, so that it sits upright and is easily seen. We tie a piece of hard cured rope around the claws of the line anchor, splicing an eye in each end. The shank end of the anchor is tied to the rope with lighter twine, so that in the case of the anchor catching in, the strain will break the twine and the anchor will come out backwards. See Fig. 27.

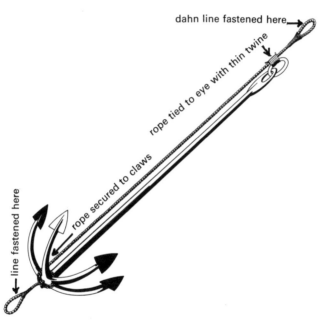

dahn line fastened here

rope tied to eye with thin twine

rope secured to claws

line fastened here

FIG. 27   Longline anchor.

The same system can be applied to anchoring on rough ground when angling from a boat with a larger anchor down. The general layout of an anchored long line is shown in Fig. 28.

Unless fishing for ray or skate exclusively, it is normal practice to shoot long line over stoney ground or along the edge of higher, rocky ground, but never right on it, as much damage can be done to hooks, stops and the main line, often resulting in the loss of much of it, through it sweeping and cutting on the sharp edges. The same applies when working on inshore grounds, although when hand hauling from a small boat it is easier to avoid damage and generally speaking, rougher grounds can be more successfully worked.

If the line does part both ends, drop an anchor or weight attached

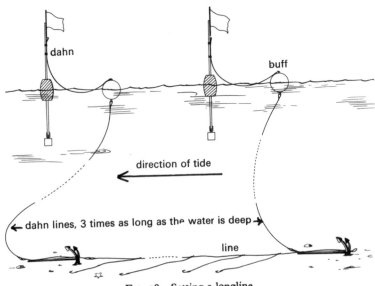

FIG. 28   Setting a longline.

to a line, buff and dahn, then "creep" for it, preferably down with the tide, with at least three to four times the length of line to the depth of water, more if possible. Four types of line creeper are shown in Fig. 29.

It is always good practice when you have lifted the line approximately halfway to the surface to have a line anchor with a rope tied into the ring and throw it as far as possible away from the side of the boat so as to come up against the line and then lift it on the anchor.

Sometimes contact can be made more easily with the line by throwing the anchor away from the bows or stern depending on how the line is leading. After lifting, the line is cut, one side being worked in, the other being dahned and buoyed. Ordinary line creepers are liable to snag in the very rough ground preferred by congers and so a length of old mooring chain tied into a rough bunch should be used. This serves just as well as the usual type of creeper and is much easier to "break out" from the rough bottom.

Another useful tip for lining when a snag is encountered is to cut the line and tie on a large buff or a bunch of small floats and a dahn. Go to the other end of the line, and if the same thing happens, leaving a fair bit of line out, cut, tie on buff and dahn again, then leave for the tide to change and run its strength. I have done this many times, leaving part of a line out overnight and even for several days in bad weather. When I return one end has usually cleared itself and it is then easy to retrieve.

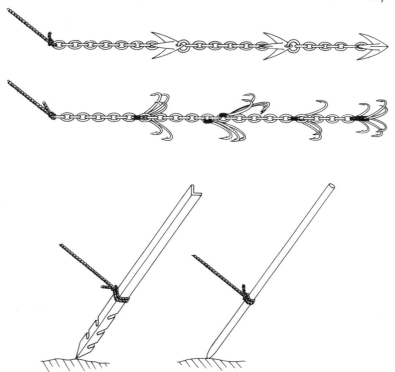

FIG. 29 Creepers. (*Top*) Line creeper or "devil" made of small heavy four-pointed grapnels joined by chain. (*Middle*) Creeper made of bunches of hooks tied closely to a length of chain. (*Bottom left*) Angle-iron with grooves cut to catch line. Line is attached one-third of the way up from base. (*Bottom right*) Iron bar, also towed on the thirds. Both bar type creepers ideal for rough ground.

When lining it is advisable to have spare dahning equipment, lines etc., ready for use at all times.

Hurricane lights used on the dahns at night are now being replaced by long life electric lamps, with either continuous or flashing lights.

Fishing for conger requires the line to be shot at dusk or any time during darkness; for other fish, including ray, darkness is not necessary.

Spiltering for Whiting

Hemp lines in 40 fathom lengths weighing one pound each are used for the main line. Hooks are straight shanked, spade ended, tinned, Mustad No. 10. The stops are around two feet to two feet two inches long of double twisted cotton, and are now purchasable from Bridport-Gundry Ltd., Dorset, although most were made on machines at

Mevagissey in the past. The stops are spaced four feet six inches on the main line, the hooks tied by reversing two half hitches and jamming against the spade end, after passing the end through the loop. Baiting is done in tubs or baths as I have previously described, being laid around clockwise, either banked up one side of the tub only or laid continuously around, requiring the tub to be turned regularly whilst shooting. Shooting should follow the same procedure as long lining, as does anchoring the line and dahning, although in the case of spilter, owing to its fineness, it can only be shot on clean ground.

I have given details of our Cornish lining methods as these can be adapted to suit requirements in other parts of the country. Perhaps a line half way between long line and spilter in size could be adapted for inshore fishing, either using a basket for storage or if using shortish stops, worked from a bath or tub, as with spilter.

There is a good market for "white" conger eel during the winter months in our country. This is conger caught on stoney or rough bottom away from the shore. Conger caught around the shores is much darker, almost black. This colour makes it less of a commercial proposition although it tastes the same, but housewives just don't like the look of it, unfortunately.

Trawl Construction

When I first started trawling I had a job to get any information on trawl construction, as we are not a trawler port here. For the beginner or amateur fisherman I'll try to describe as simply as possible how to make and repair small trawls, in case you may be in the same position as I was a few years ago. I have not given specific measurements or patterns of any trawls, as the beginner should first buy a net suitable for his area and boat, then I hope with the help of the following notes, familiarise himself with the construction of his net, so that if any section becomes damaged he can mend or replace it himself. It must be remembered that here at Mevagissey we often work on very dirty bottom in thirty to thirty-seven fathoms of water, and the water is very clear most of the time. If you live in an area where there is plenty of clean ground suitable for trawling, it may be a lot easier to catch trawl fish owing to the water being much cloudier than in our particular area.

Basically, a trawl is a tapering net bag towed along the bottom. For flatfish, the headline is low and well forward of the footrope; this is called cover. For trawls made to catch white fish (cod, whiting, haddock etc.) the headline is a lot higher and the cover is proportionately less. This trawl needs to be towed faster than for flatfish and needs quite a lot more horsepower to work efficiently.

A trawl is made up of several pieces of net which are either sewed or laced together. See Fig. 30a and 30b.

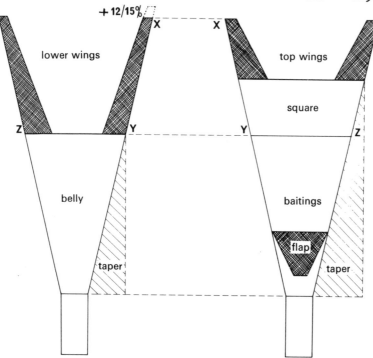

FIG. 30a Top and bottom sections of trawl. Cod end is constructed of either double or single heavier twine.

It is important to note that in the diagram of the trawl, the total length of the square and top wings equals the length of the lower wings.

This is not the case in practice, as the bottom wings should be twelve per cent to fifteen per cent longer and the slack taken up in the seam X.Y. and is necessary to allow the lower wing to lift properly and not restrict the meshes.

All sections of a trawl are sewed together point to point, just as you would do if you were sewing a piece of mending net in a hole. Trawls are so designed that they can be sewn together this way, therefore the widest section of the belly equals the narrowest end of the square, mesh for mesh ZY, YZ. Where the cod end joins the belly and baitings, again the numbers of meshes are equal, mesh for mesh, so it is easy to see that the taper or decrease on both belly and baitings must be the same in each case. The tapers of the square may be less than the rest of the trawl, but for a good job it should be about the same.

To breed lower wings, which is far less wasteful than cutting them out of sheet netting, it can be seen in Fig. 30c that the wing is bred

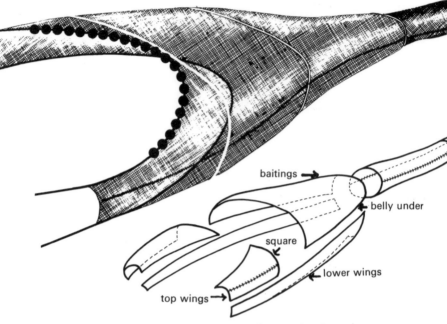

FIG. 30b Assembled trawl from netting shown in 30a.

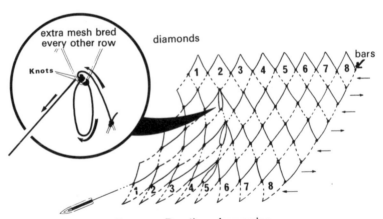

FIG. 30c Breeding a lower wing.

down leaving a bar one side, diamonds on the other. To maintain the eight meshes across, you will see it is necessary to add one more mesh or point to every other row bred, to allow for the decrease of a bar every row on the other side.

The wing should be started at the widest end, say 30 meshes. If it is to taper to ten meshes and is to be twenty feet long then you will have to lose twenty meshes over twenty feet, i.e., one mesh per foot, therefore watch out that every foot in length of net bred, you put in two rows of plain breeding over and back without the extra mesh, which will give you your decrease.

Top wings are usually cut out of net, which is wasteful but is quick to do, and as they are usually of smaller mesh than bottom wings take proportionately longer to breed by hand. Top wings like lower wings have one side which is cut on the bar all the way. This is later seized to the headline along the bar, the same way as the straight edge of the lower wing is seized to the balch line. Being shorter than the lower wings, but much wider where they join the squares, i.e., having a greater number of meshes, then the taper is also much sharper, and should be traced down very carefully before you finally cut. To me, a top wing is the hardest part of a trawl to make, as mistakes can easily be made when cutting the decrease unless you hold the net securely A to B Fig. 31.

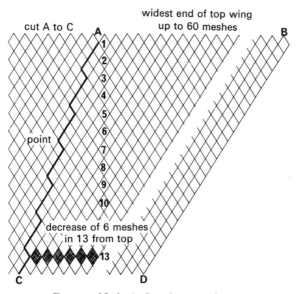

FIG. 31 Method of cutting top wing.

You will notice the run of net follows the numbers one—thirteen, and that by cutting down three bars and then stepping in to leave a point gives a loss or decrease of six meshes in the length of thirteen straight meshes. The bottom of the wing C to D terminates squarely across on the diamonds or points. It is important to remember that half a mesh is lost on every row, side B to D, therefore cutting a bar in the opposite direction in line A to C gives you an immediate loss of six whole meshes; whereas, if the net were square on side B to D only three meshes would be lost by cutting as in A to C. If you require a more gradual decrease, increase the number of meshes cut on the bar as in 1, 2, 3 of cut A to B and have less points.

It is a good plan to mark mesh A with a piece of twine, count down your proposed cut with your fingers to mesh C which should also be marked. When you have found a suitable combination of side bars and points, and you have had little experience of net cutting, mark each point with a little piece of sellotape or twine so that you can follow your cut without deviating.

Bellies and baiting should be of equal length, width and taper. Take your sheet of net, Fig. 32, and count your meshes across the

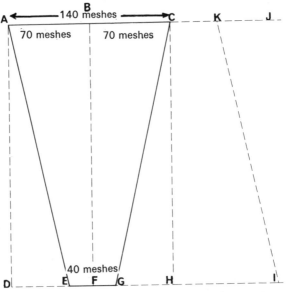

FIG. 32   Cutting out belly or baitings from sheet netting.

widest end, say one hundred and forty. Mark the centre at seventy meshes across with a piece of twine. Follow that row of meshes down vertically to point F, also count out to edges C and H to check correctness of point F. We require forty meshes at E to G, therefore count out twenty meshes from F to meshes E and G.

From the diagram you will see that fifty meshes have to be lost each side, so you will then run down line A to E to find a suitable combination of bars and side points to achieve this cut on the taper needed.

Having cut A to E, run down C to G carefully before cutting, as you are proceeding on the opposite taper and a mistake can be easily made. It is better to have a mesh or two over the number required at E to G, as these can be sewn into the seam later, rather than cut your meshes short.

If your sheet is wide enough, cut your second piece by reversing the procedure in Fig. 32, using cut G to C as a side, having the widest part of the net at line G to I, the narrowest at C to J. By cutting the first sheet properly, only a second cut will be required for the second sheet, line I to K. Do not cut dotted line C to H on any account, unless you wish to square the surplus net up for another use, as it is merely put in the diagram to illustrate the vertical square run of the net at that point.

The flap in your trawl should be made of minimum mesh, seventy millimetres for man made fibres, seventy-five millimetres for material made of natural fibres, i.e., cotton, hemp, etc., and sewn in after belly and baitings are joined. It is good practice to use cotton or hemp net for this purpose, as it sinks when movement of the trawl stops prior to hauling in a small boat, and thereby traps any fish anxious to vacate the cod end!

The flap at its widest part should be sewn to the back or baitings of the trawl, mesh for mesh, from seam to seam, making sure there are no meshes missed, especially at the corners. The sides of the flap are cut down on the bar, which is then laced along the run of bars directly in line with it on the belly of the trawl. Make sure you do not make the flap too long, thereby leaving too small a hole for a large fish to pass through when first caught, see Fig. 33.

Obviously if you feel confident enough to make a trawl, you will have observed how others are constructed and laced to head lines and balch lines, but here are a few useful tips.

When you have sewn top wings, square belly and back together, also the bottom wings and belly, take the edge and end of the top wing and square, Fig. 34, and tie them up at their full length.

Do the same with the end of the lower wing, on the side it is to be sewn into the seam; then find where you have sewn the lower wing onto the belly and hang at B.

If you have used a different coloured twine for sewing the pieces together it will make your job easier. You will then be able to incorporate the slack either mostly along from C to B or equally along the whole length A to B.

The ends of the wings should be reinforced with thick twine knot for knot, as should the head breast and bosom, which is set on the

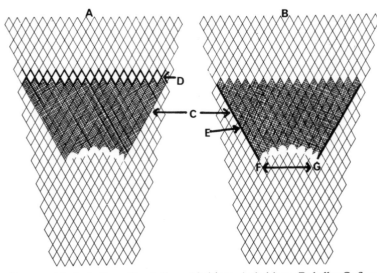

FIG. 33   Method of attaching belly and baitings. A: baitings; B: belly; C: flap; D: sewed mesh for mesh, top of flap only; E: sewed down on bars, leaving reasonable gap at F to G.

relevant ropes on the points, not like the wings, which are fastened to the ropes along the bars.

The bosom and the head breast are formed with the net left between the lower wings and the top wings respectively. This is set on the halves, i.e. a mesh of three inches knot to knot (one and a half inch bar) would be set on half its fully extended width one and a half inch between points, or to make it plainer, four such meshes would be set along four and a half inches of rope.

When setting the net to a footrope, measure the completed seam from A to B, Fig. 34, then place that measurement on to one side of your footrope A—B Fig. 35. Allow an inch or two of slack for your bosom, i.e. measure the length of the bosom, deduct a couple of inches, then place another mark, C. Fig. 35, C to D should equal A to B.

When seizing the balch line to the footrope, seizings C and B should be made large and distinctive, with plenty of smaller seizings between. The balch line should be seized down equally along the lengths A to B, C to D.

Cod ends should be made four meshes wider than needed. The two extra meshes are incorporated in the seam each side, the same as the rest of the seams or selvedges as they are sometimes called, which are laced together and include two whole meshes from each side to be sewn together.

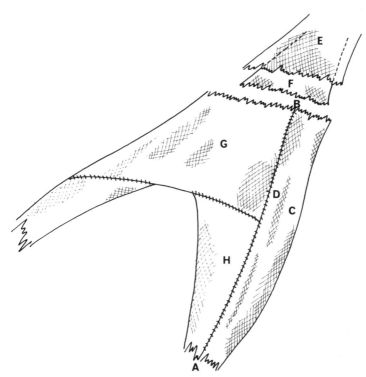

FIG. 34 Joining lower wing to top wing and square. A–B: completed seam; C: lower wing; D: slack; E: back; F: belly; G: square; H: top wing.

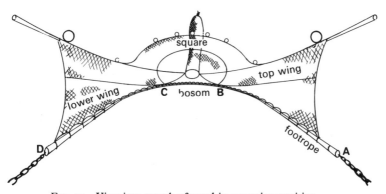

FIG. 35 View into mouth of trawl in operating position.

Footropes and Bridles

It is advisable to lace pieces of old dumper or large lorry inner tubes on to the bottom of the cod end to absorb wear if a lot of rubbish is caught in the trawl. Further up, old pieces of net can be sewn on as chafers. All chafers, whether net or rubber, should overlap the next one down to protect the seizings against wear.

Choice of footropes depends on the size of trawl, ground to be worked and horsepower available. For inshore boats, four types of footrope are shown Fig. 36.

Weight must be adjusted to suit particular needs and is a matter of trial and error for the fisherman, who must strike a happy medium between the weight and digging power of the footrope, the buoyancy of the headline when properly mounted with floats, and the tendency for his trawl to lift depending on its construction and the speed at which it is towed.

Some trawlers work very long bridles from their boards to the trawl. Forty fathoms is the most I have heard of, while others use as little as three fathoms. If the ground you intend to work is sandy and uneven, with banks and depressions, the doors should be as close to the trawl as possible, otherwise the trawl will cut into a bank, fill with sand and may become impossible to haul.

A footrope constructed like D Fig. 36 is ideal for this type of ground. Footrope C is heavier, having a greater number of discs, and can be overlaid with pieces of chain if required and is suitable for flatter harder ground.

Types A and B are suitable for light trawling, B having greater strength and being less liable to damage.

When hauling gear by hand, or with the help of a capstan, it is often a good idea to have your bridles at least of a length equal to the depth of water you are trawling in, provided the type of ground allows this. You can then get the boards up and secured before hauling the trawl.

Bridles can be of wire or combination rope, and have a great shepherding effect on bottom dwelling fish. We use a set up here which consists of a long towing bridle but a comparatively short bridle to the headline. The swivel is also a great help as it enables the turns to be taken out of the gear after it has been hauled round a capstan Fig. 37.

We use a small pair of G links (heavy seine net links would do)—one on the wire backstrop of the board and one in the eye of the bridle. Also in the eye of the bridle is spliced a strong synthetic rope which is passed over the top of the door. After it has been allowed to hang slackly, it is fixed to the towing bracket with a claw hitch. Fig. 38.

When our doors are up, we take the strain on the rope, then unclip the bridle from one door, hauling it around a whipping drum. As soon

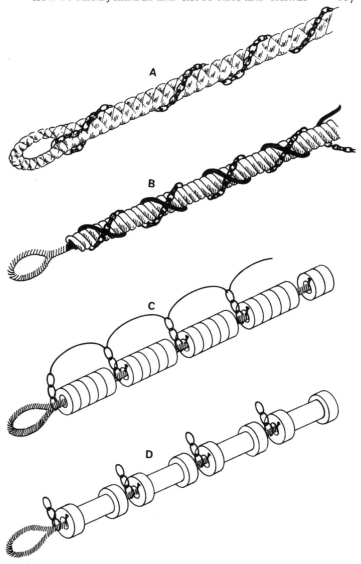

FIG. 36   Trawl footropes. A: soft laid large rope covered with light chain laid around from end to end (suitable for light trawling); B: wire or light chain core, covered with light rope and overlaid with light chain. Car tyres cut in continuous strips and turned against themselves can be used instead of the chain; C: wire core with rubber discs and wire and chain threaded over. Nails driven through prevent discs from slipping to centre; D: same principle as C but using heavy rubber hosepipe between discs. In both C and D the balch line is fastened to the chains which cuts down wear on siezings.

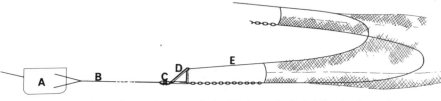

FIG. 37   Use of triangle and swivel with long single bridle. A: door; B: 30 fathom wire bridle; C: large swivel; D: iron triangle; E: head bridle (combination rope light wire, or synthetic rope).

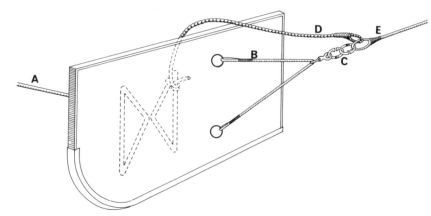

FIG. 38   Method of attaching and undoing bridle from door for hauling by capstan or hand. A: towing bridle; B: wire backstraps; C: detachable links; D: rope attached to bridle and door bracket; E: bridle.

as enough slack is inboard, the bridle should be clipped back immediately to the board so as to avoid crossing with the other wire during hauling.

When the strain of the trawl has been taken on one bridle, the other can be unclipped and hauled either mechanically or by hand, depending on the amount of weight in the trawl. Hauling with the strain on one bridle stretches a trawl one side and should be avoided if there is any weight in it.

If clips are used which are of doubtful strength, and a strong rope is used from the bridle to the towing bracket, then if the bridles should undo while hauling, the rope will still take the strain of the bridle if properly hitched to the towing bracket.

On the *We'll Try* we have adopted a semi stern trawling method of working by using the board attachments I have just mentioned. We shoot from the side, the bridles are coiled on the deck and stream away until the gear is towing squarely from the stern. Then the boards are released and after the warps are levelled, towing is commenced Fig. 39.

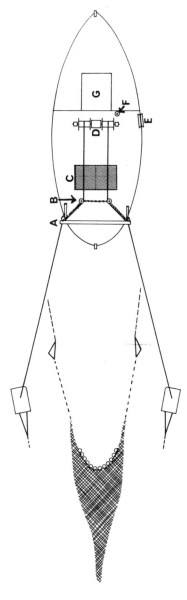

FIG. 39   Shooting from *We'll Try*. A: gantry; B: blocks on chain carrying warps square to winch barrels; C: engine cover; D: winch; E: roller set on rail; F: snatch block in line with starboard whipping barrel; G: wheelhouse.

Hints On Hauling

When hauling we come back square over our gear, which is being pulled back by winch. With the boards up, we detach the first bridle, hauling it over the roller on the starboard side, and passing it through the snatch block sited opposite the starboard whipping drum, then around the drum. It is clipped back onto its board and the other bridle is unclipped, flipped round the stern, then hauled either by hand or via snatch blocks B to the port whipping barrel.

The bag is lifted in on a four part purchase slung from the starboard side of the gantry. We also have a derrick slung from the centre of the gantry which plumbs over each side if needed for additional lifting power.

We are also able to lift from the top of the after gantry legs if needed by attaching blocks to the ends, which jut out for this purpose. Being a "double ender", we cannot haul or shoot our net over the stern, so we have compromised. If we had an overhanging transom stern, then we should work larger blocks and use orthodox wire backstrops and G links to make the hauling a continuous process.

The two blocks carrying the wire warps out to the ends of the gantry are fitted in T pieces, which can be slid along the pipe to any position by undoing the Alun keys holding them in place. We can therefore tow from each quarter from one quarter, or centrally.

Going through only two blocks, there is little strain on the warps when hauling unless the gear is fast, therefore hardly any wear has so far been noticed on the blocks and not any on the warps, which can easily be spread by hand when hauling as we have no automatic spreader on the winch.

Feathering For Mackerel

Lastly I should mention feathering for mackerel, as much of this has been done around the South Cornish coast during the last three winters and has been a good source of income for fishermen who would otherwise have been hard pushed to earn a living here winter time.

Unless you have a lot of time at your disposal, it is best to purchase good scotch mackerel feathers as advertised at times in *Fishing News*. If the feathers wear off quickly, pieces of different coloured electric flex covering can be substituted by slipping the hook off and sliding a piece of flex down the shank, leaving the point and barb of the hook well uncovered Fig. 40.

The Looe fishermen make up their own sets of lures by using the pieces of flex exclusively, while we at Mevagissey prefer feathers still.

One interesting development has arisen at Looe though in the use of feather lines for mackerel in the winter time. As large mackerel have a tendency to stop the feathers going after a few have been hooked,

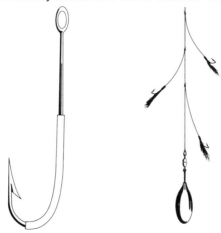

FIG. 40   (*Right*) Mackerel feathers with a 1–2 lb. lead weight attached by means
of a heavy swivel. Hooks and feathers are set 5–6 inches apart. (*Left*) Using
coloured electrical wire insulation in place of feathers.

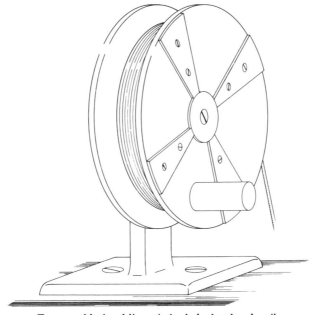

FIG. 41   Mackerel line winder bolted to boat's rail.

more weight has been used to counteract this. Consequently, fingers
became more and more tender, arms more tired; so a wheel has been

developed which is fixed to the rail of the boat on which the feather line is wound. The line is allowed to run until it is either stopped by being fished or the bottom; then it is wound up again by a single handle, on the side like a giant fishing reel.

When the feathers are reached, they are lifted into the boat and the mackerel unhooked in the normal way.

The wheel should be about one and a half feet in diameter, two inches or three inches wide, with one handle and the whole thing should be either pegged into the boat's rail or fixed with thumb screw in under, like the fittings of a table tennis net frame. When fitting it make sure the wheel runs freely to allow maximum speed when the line is run out (Fig. 41). Mackerel are now washed and neatly packed aboard our boats as soon as they are caught. This greatly improves their quality when later they are offered for sale to the public.

Chapter 17

Just his share

DOWN here in Cornwall we are still a long way from the rest of
the British Isles, and most important, far removed from the major
centres of population. The railways, which in the past carried a large
proportion of Cornish fish up to Bristol, the Midlands, the South of
England and London, have now found it uneconomical unless a very
high carriage rate is charged. So they have lost all that trade to the
road transport people who in turn are having to increase their rates
to cover the mounting overheads incurred in their efforts to stay in
business and show a reasonable profit on the capital invested.

All the increased costs incurred by the shore-based sides of the
business have also to be met by fishermen, either directly through his
increased running costs, the additional costs of his gear, or indirectly
through a lower nett price received for his catch, whether he has a
large boat, a small one, works in his own right, or is employed on a
share basis.

Where a port is reasonably close to a heavily populated area, the
cost of transporting fish to market is considerably cheaper; usually
a large fleet of boats is based at the port and the large amount of fish
landed also greatly contributes to lower distribution costs, while the
number of wholesalers attracted there creates a competitive atmosphere
which helps to keep up a fair average price.

We all know the fish trade is unpredictable, and is subject to fluctua-
tions caused by supply and demand. But this neither benefits the
fisherman, the wholesaler, the retailer nor the customer in the long run.
While these problems to a large extent can be dealt with satisfactorily
at a major fishing centre, it is not so easy for the Cornish fisherman,
who works from small harbours, even coves. His fish has to be trans-
ported from these places to a centre, then handled again for distribution
up country. Here at Mevagissey we now find we are in a much healthier
position so far as the returns from our catches are concerned than we
were a few years ago; also our prospects for the future are much
rosier. This is largely because of our formation of a Co-operative
Company. As I have previously mentioned, forming a Co-op is not
easy, but we have found it well worthwhile in the long run. Only good

can come out of such a move so long as a group can stick together during the rough patches as well as during the smooth going.

At the time of writing, a Cornwall Fishermen's Co-operative has just been formed, its members coming from every fishing community in Cornwall*. As this develops in the future, no doubt fishing in the County will greatly benefit directly by its formation. We as an existing Co-operative at Mevagissey look forward to working with it and perhaps, when details have been fully worked out, becoming an integral part of it.

I cannot stress too highly the value of the work done by the White Fish Authority to the fishing community and its allied trades. Quite apart from the grants and loans on new fishing boats, equipment and in some cases fishing gear, if it is required to fit out a new boat, they have a splendid advisory service, which is prepared to give advice and practical help on every aspect of catching, processing, marketing and distribution of fish. We have found nothing is too large or too small for them to help and advise us on; it must also be remembered, a great amount of work is also done by their research establishments into every aspect of deep water and inshore fishing. This ranges from shell fish cultivation and conservation, exploring potential fishing grounds, testing fishing gear, tagging and recording fish movements, research into processing and marketing fish, and also to improving and testing new fishing methods, to mention but a few of their activities. Anyone wishing to know more about The White Fish Authority's grants and loans schemes, or their advisory services etc., should first contact their local W.F.A. Officer, whose office can usually be traced through a telephone directory. He will be pleased to advise on and discuss every aspect of any particular need or problem.

The introduction of the Fishing Limits Act in 1964 on the 30th September, which extended our Fishery Limits to twelve miles was enthusiastically welcomed by inshore fishermen everywhere.

In the discussions which the government undertook with various fishery bodies such as the Fisheries Organization Society, representations were made on behalf of inshore fishermen to the effect that no concessions should be granted to foreigners in respect of traditional fishing rights and even if they were, they should be subject to phase-out requirements after a period of years. Inevitably, these representations were not accepted by the government, which presumably for political or diplomatic reasons, conceded certain rights to foreign fishing vessels.

Legislation, as finally passed, provided for the total enclosure of large bays up to twenty-four miles in length with straight lines, as against a maximum limit of ten miles under previous legislation.

*This Society is now established as Cornwall Fishermen Ltd.

It is very difficult to assess the benefits obtained from the extension of the limit around Cornwall, as we differ greatly from other parts of the country both geographically and in the methods and fisheries pursued. There is no doubt however that the extension of the limits can do nothing but good to the inshore fisherman eventually, especially in areas previously heavily fished by foreign vessels.

One of the most interesting effects of the extension of limits, coupled with assistance from the W.F.A. has been the growth of the trawler fleet at Plymouth in Devon, right on the borders of Devon and Cornwall. Brixham, farther up on the South coast of Devonshire, has also experienced a boom in their trawling industry. A co-operative was formed there that has virtually a one hundred per cent membership. This took over the job of marketing the total landings of the port, and since then they have planned and started on major reconstruction work to their fish market and harbour.

As an example of the "go ahead" attitude of Brixham fishermen, three boats from that port changed over to mid-water trawling for mackerel and pilchards in the winter of 1969-70. Two friends of mine, Cliff Pender, originally from Mousehole in Cornwall, and Johnny Perks of Brixham operate two large trawlers from that port, and have met with considerable success by pair trawling, whilst another trawler has been successfully mid-water trawling on its own. Although originally intending to catch mackerel by this method, they have been able to catch and land substantial quantities of pilchards, which has enabled the canning factory at Newlyn to keep going this winter, instead of closing up which was originally anticipated.

As an example of what progress can be made I give the figures of the growth of Mevagissey Fisheries Ltd. over the first four years of trading.

Share Capital £3,200 approx.   100 members

Paid to members for fish	Sales of fish	Dividend paid on Share capital	Surplus repaid to members pro rata to carriage paid by them
1966 £15,151	£19,183	5%	£283
Share Capital £3,519 slight increase in membership			
1967 £32,698	£40,788	8%	£2,321
Share Capital £3,288 a decrease owing to retirements etc.			
1968 £32,192	£43,163	8%	£1,943
Figures not available for share capital as audit uncompleted			
1969 £38,781	£48,089	8%	£3,209

We cannot always foresee the future accurately, or we would be more than human, but provided the inshore fishermen helps himself, he will always find others to help him, and the future of the industry will depend more and more on better co-operation between fishermen, merchants and various advisory bodies connected with the industry. There is no reason why the inshore fishing industry should not go from strength to strength, as the fisherman nowadays has a commodity second to none in quality to offer to the trade—provided it is properly handled and marketed.

When I first came to Mevagissey I was as green as a lettuce leaf, but I set my heart on going fishing and more by luck than judgment I managed to achieve that ambition.

I had left the world I knew and joined a community I could not then understand for the life of me. They were men who knew only one job, one environment. Their lives, and the lives of their families were completely involved in earning a living from the sea. As in any community there were the strong and the weak, the intelligent and the simple, the honest and the dishonest. They had the one common bond though—they were fishermen, and slowly over the years I have been able to understand them and get to know them, each one, as fine individualists.

The sad part for me has been the number of men who have retired and died since I started sixteen years ago. The big boats have nearly all gone, as have many of the older fishermen. Soon there will not be any of the old men left to carry on the tales so often told in the past around the quay or over a pint in one of the locals on Saturday dinner time or a stormy night in the winter.

I called up to Plymouth just after Christmas to see an old pal George Launder, who has fished all his life, and now owns a couple of trawlers with his two partners. We were having a drink in the "Dolphin" and I casually asked him if he had enjoyed Christmas.

"I was nearly put inside for Christmas," he solemnly told me "It was a . . . . near thing I can tell you Stan".

I quickly bought another pint all round and waited as George lit a cigarette and stuck it to his top lip, where it would stay, miraculously defying gravity until replaced by another from his seemingly inexhaustible supply carried beneath the cover of his barked jumper.

He pushed his battered trilby hat up an inch, then after a good swig of his beer he told me the yarn.

Just before Christmas he had been asked by an owner at Plymouth if he would do a towing job. It was to take a large catamaran up to Brixham. Now George had a lot of pals up there, so although it wasn't an overpaid job he took it, and on arrival looked forward to a good session with his mates before he set sail for Plymouth again.

George had been given exact details of where the catamaran was moored, so on the appointed day they collected her from her mooring very early in the morning and set off in moderate weather for Brixham. All went well and when George made fast the two craft alongside the quay there, he was met by three gentlemen who asked him if he was George Launder.

"Yes, that's me" Says George "I suppose you've come to collect the boat".

"Yes" replies one of them "We've come to collect you as well, and I must warn you anything you say will be taken down and may be used in evidence against you".

I was assured at this stage by one of George's crew that what he said then would never have been taken anywhere, let alone have been used in evidence; but sure enough the three chaps were police officers and they had come to arrest George on a charge of stealing the catamaran.

George refused to leave his boat, so was left in charge of one of the men while the other two went off to phone the owner who had chartered George for the job.

When they came back they told him that the boat he was to have towed up was still moored at Plymouth, and why had he taken someone else's?

Poor old George spent most of the afternoon explaining he had made a mistake while his pals up on the quay who had already started celebrating Christmas kept shouting down.

"Good old George, we knew they'd catch you if you kept pinching boats," or "How long do you think you'll get this time?"

These humorous and ribald remarks didn't improve George's case, but in the end they let him go on condition he took the boat straight back to Plymouth and reported in the next day which he managed to do in spite of worsening weather.

He made doubly sure he got the right one at his second attempt though!

They're a fine bunch of chaps at Plymouth. Although primarily a trawler port, they have their ups and downs as in any other place, and when we worked from there for a season we had nothing but help and kindness extended to us during our whole stay. The same when we worked from Newlyn and Swansea. It's something you've got to experience to understand, and I'd go as far as to say wherever a fisherman goes amongst fishermen he's amongst friends, whether he's the owner of a plank or an eighty footer.

People often ask me why I went to sea and started fishing. I reply because its there, it's as simple as that. I suppose people who climb mountains because they are there, act for much the same reasons. I get great satisfaction from the job, like hanging it out in poor weather to get an extra drag in, knowing that if you don't you won't be out the next day anyway, then making everything fast before we go scuttling off as hard as we can for the shelter of the harbour.

A chap who could wield a pen far better than I can would no doubt be able to wax long and eloquently about the changing faces of the sea and the coastline around our part of Cornwall. I personally never tire of looking around and observing things.

The tiny swarms of life gathered amongst the flotsam carried in the shed of tide, often many miles from land. The great shoals of basking sharks that visit us during the summer; seeing them jump clear of the water to stand on their tails before falling sideways again, sending great sheets of water away as they hit the surface. Whether these antics are sheer exuberance or an attempt to get rid of the lice which cluster thickly around their gills I do not know.

Fine weather or foul there's always something to see, something to think about. The job of trawling to me is the most interesting of all the types of fishing I have ever done. I am always trying to improve our results, but there is always the satisfaction of finding a little bit of ground no one else has worked. This is often accompanied by several fasteners and a lot of needle work, but once you've got it taped off, its yours, and jolly useful when fish is scarce.

It's very easy to remember all the good things attached to fishing. The big catches, the fine long summer days and nights, the companionship, the humorous episodes etc., but there's another side too. The long spells of bad weather, the hours spent making a new trawl, only to lose it perhaps a few days after you have shot it for the first time. The long line trips, often in dirty weather when you don't catch enough to cover your expenses. The fleet of ray trammels towed away or cut to ribbons by a foreign trawler during the night. Two thirds of a fleet of crab pots lost during a prolonged southerly blow. The engine that broke down in the middle of a good spell of weather when fish was plentiful.

All these things tip the scales the other way. To a few they tip them too far, while to most fishermen things still seem to balance up nicely in spite of everything; and fishing's still the best job in the world to most of them, although many won't admit it! There's still plenty of room out there, there's all sorts of fish. What more could a chap ask for than "Just his Share?"

Glossary of local terms

Allright?	Means either good morning, afternoon, evening
Backing	Main line
Bark	Cure gear in boiled Borneo cutch
Bib	Rock pouting
Black Danny	Black-backed gull
Buff	Inflatable buoy, canvas or plastic
Bumps	Cuttle fish
Bump tide	Bottom or top of tide
Catched down	Dahn line swept around, then pulled down with the tide if hitched in the bottom, usually taking buffs, etc. with it
Coble	Bunch of corks used to float drift nets
Cowshurney	Yellow-tinged water where mackerel are found in quantity early in the year
Creep	To tow a devil, to retrieve lost line
Creeper	Small line anchor
Cuddy	Small forrard cabin
Cutch	Net preservative
Dappling	Softening, easing (of weather)
Devil	Hooks, etc., used to creep line off the bottom
Dimpling	Halflight—morning or evening
Dog mocking the sun	Reflection of sun on water vapour, heralding the approach of bad weather, usually from the South
Doo	Two
Dree	Three
Ess	Yes
Fast	Hitched on bottom
Fiddler	Crayfish
Frizzer	Very gusty conditions
Gavorick	Spider crab
Geet	Large
Gingeing	Four or six-part cotton stop, used to reinforce single stop just above hook when lining in the old days
Graper	A long-shanked four or five clawed anchor
Green oil	Thin creosote
Grope	Motion in water, before or after bad spell of weather
Guff	A lot, or surfeit, usually of fish

Hallelulah day	Saturday
Hector	Waste salted pilchards used as dog baits
Helem	Helm
Hitch or fastener	Trawling term for obstruction on seabed
Joe	A gullible person. Usually one to be taken advantage of, especially if money is involved!
Jinney	Mechanical linehauler
Marmaduke	Foresail
Nigging	Pulling or jerking
Norsel or nozzel	Short piece of double-twisted cotton used to set a drift net to its headrope
Oily birds	Mother Carey's chickens
Patent	Anti-fouling preparations
Piggy dog	Blue Spur dogfish
Planet	Thunder cloud or thunderstorm
Punt	Any stout rowing boat which is sculled from the stern by a single paddle
Quarter	Small cock crab
Riddle	Shoal of pilchards swimming and jumping
Row hounds	Rough dogs. Greater and lesser spotted dogfish
Sclowed	Gouged, scored, scruffed, grazed
Shet or shetting	To shoot gear, shooting gear
Shill	Fish scale
Shiny eye	Poor man's cod—a species of small pouting-like fish
Shot fish, shotten fish	Fish that is in poor condition, having recently spawned. Applied to both herring and pilchard
Sign	Birds working on a shoal of fish
Skimming up	Reaching the bottom of a drift net when first going to work by pulling up the end line
Skit	Sea spray or any kind of drink
Spiltering	Form of longlining, using fine hemp or cotton lines, light-twisted cotton stops and small spade-ended hooks specifically for catching whiting
Splat	Shoal of fish, spot of oil on the water, or a bunch or group of anything
Spot	Shoal of fish
Stink hound	Tope
Stoit	Fish jumping singly
Stop	Line from backing to hook
Strap	The rope, usually $3\frac{1}{2}$ to 4 fathoms long attaching the coble to the headline of a drift net. Or is sometimes applied to large conger eel
Strap up	To come tight, to stop under the strain, entangled
Taching	Join, usually between two drift nets
Tatie diggers	People who come from inland to pursue fishing for a living
That's av em	That is it
Tight as a drum	Gear strained to the limit

Top notch	Best fisherman or best crew. Hard working. Derived from opening a notched throttle to give maximum performance of engine
Tow rag	Salted cod
Twitchet	Piece of odd twine or line
Wan	One
Whip	Small conger eel
Wink	A "shot" pilchard
Willem	Turbulence caused by a diving fish or propeller